DANGEROUS MOONLIGHT

D1647073

For Lynn, what started as revenge for the way he had broken-up her sister's marriage, soon became love for Andreas Stephanos. But was her love enough to keep him when it appeared that he was merely settling for second best?

DANGEROUS MOONLIGHT

BY

KAY THORPE

MILLS & BOON LIMITED
15–16 BROOK'S MEWS
LONDON W1A 1DR

First published in Great Britain 1985
by Mills & Boon Limited

© Kay Thorpe 1985

Australian copyright 1985
Philippine copyright 1986
This edition 1986

ISBN 0 263 75284 4

Set in Monophoto Plantin 10 on 11 pt.
01-0286 – 55148

Made and printed in Great Britain by
Richard Clay (The Chaucer Press) Ltd,
Bungay, Suffolk

CHAPTER ONE

EMERGING through the doors in the wake of a German party, Lynn paused for a moment to orientate herself, blinking in the strong sunlight. Her sunglasses were in her handbag. Putting down her suitcase, she took them out and put them on. That was better. Now she could see without squinting.

As the hostess who had greeted their flight had said, the coaches were lined up across the road from the terminal. Some were already full and beginning to move out. Lifting her suitcase again, Lynn crossed over to where several couriers with clipboards were directing tourists in the direction of their appropriate transport.

'The Amalia?' she asked the nearest green-jacketed girl, and received a distracted smile as the latter ran her eye down the list.

'Top row, second from end. Noel will meet you.' The smile came again, turned on automatically as if on cue. 'Have a good holiday.'

Not so much a holiday as a means to an end, Lynn reflected as she moved in the direction indicated. The package deal was convenient, to say nothing of cheaper in the long run. The air fare to Athens alone would have cost her almost two thirds of the total sum she had paid. This way she not only had a base in the very area she wanted to cover but all the advantages of an 'A' class hotel to boot. Considering the heat now at three o'clock on this May afternoon, the air-conditioning was going to be a boon. Her own bathroom, too. One would hardly get that in a taverna.

Roughing it might be all right for some; she preferred her creature comforts.

Male this time, another of the green-jacketed tour hosts moved to greet her, stretching out a hand for her suitcase with a smile that certainly looked warm enough.

'Let me,' he offered. 'You must be Miss Renford. We only have the one single this trip.'

'Lynn,' she said, smiling back. 'I gather you're Noel?'

He laughed, blue eyes sparkling at her. 'My fame goeth before me!'

'A couple of hundred yards, anyway.' She slanted a glance at the tanned, handsome face under its shock of dark gold hair as they moved towards the waiting coaches. About twenty-six, twenty-seven, she hazarded. Just right for her own twenty-four years if she had been at all interested in the kind of holiday affair he could no doubt offer. A girl on her own was fair game to all, friends had warned her when the trip was first mooted. Only if the encouragement was there, Lynn had replied. She still felt the same. It was up to the individual.

'First time in Greece?' he asked, and she shook her head.

'I was in Thessaly in September. First time in Athens, though, unless you can count one day sightseeing off a cruise ship when I was twelve. I understand the hotel is only about an hour or so from here.'

'Depends who's doing the driving. The highway between here and the Canal is one of the busiest in the country.'

Lynn pulled a face. 'That doesn't sound so good. The brochure promised sun and scenery. It said nothing about traffic.'

'Where we are there isn't any. Not to count. Once you're away from the Canal it's back to nature.' He handed over her suitcase to a man in dark trousers and white shirt whom Lynn assumed was the driver of the coach, added, 'I'd take the first seat inside the door if I were you. We have to wait half an hour for another flight coming in and the air doesn't come on unless the engine's running.'

'Thanks,' she said. 'I'll do that.'

The coach was already almost half full. The cynosure of all eyes, Lynn gave a general smile of greeting and stowed her carry-on bag on the upper shelf before taking her seat. Noel had returned to his former position and was directing further passengers towards the coach. Two middle-aged couples, obviously travelling together, took their seats opposite when they came aboard, immediately opening every window within reach in an effort to create a through-draught from the doorway and reduce the interior temperature.

Looking through her near window, Lynn caught the eye of the driver standing below, registering his unabashed appraisal without allowing a flicker of expression to cross her own face. Most Greek women were dark-haired. It stood to reason that a natural blonde would attract attention.

She was being unduly modest, and she knew it. Her particular combination of wide-set green eyes, small straight nose and generously curved mouth gave her an advantage to which the shoulder-length pale hair could only contribute in part. A bane sometimes, she was bound to admit. This coming fortnight all she wanted was to be left alone to further her research into Greek history. The Corinthian isthmus and Peloponnese peninsula were steeped in more than four thousand years of it.

She was going to need to stick to a definite itinerary

in order to fit in everything she wanted to see, she reflected, turning away from the glass. Two weeks wasn't a long time. The regular tours from the hotel itself would be out. She had tried those in Thessaly and it hadn't worked. Too much time on the road and in tourist gift traps and too little on the ancient sites themselves. The best way, someone had told her when it was too late, was to hire one of the local taxis for a whole day at a time with a prior arrangement over price. A good driver would go anywhere she asked and stay as long as required. Cost would be the deciding factor, but it wouldn't hurt to enquire.

The sun had moved round far enough to find the corner of her window. Reaching up, she pulled on the roller blind strap but it refused to budge. One of the men opposite got up and came to help, leaning across her to free the blind and fasten it in position halfway down. Lynn thanked him gratefully, catching a cynical glance from his partner across the aisle as she did so. Not the first time she had been cast in the role of provocateur, she acknowledged with a cynicism of her own. Probably not the last either. Being a lone female had its drawbacks.

It was more like fifty minutes before the rest of the awaited passengers began to put in an appearance. Noel followed the last of them up the coach steps, grinning ruefully at Lynn as he pulled the door to behind him.

'Flight was late in. It's always happening.'

'Hardly your fault,' she responded. 'Providing we get there in time for dinner I don't suppose anyone minds too much.'

'Want to bet?' He winked at her, then turned to pick up the microphone attached to the dashboard in front of the courier's seat, switching it on with a flick of his thumb. 'Can everyone hear me at the back?'

The murmur of voices seemed to signal affirmation. At any rate he took it as such. 'Sorry for the delay, folks. We'll be on our way as soon as I've run through the list. Best way is if I come down the aisle and tick of your names as I reach you. We don't want to leave anybody behind.'

The process took several minutes. With the doors shut the air was rapidly becoming stifling. Lynn opened her own window a fraction but it made little difference. She was thankful when the driver climbed into his seat from the opposite side of the cab and switched on the engine, feeling the air beginning to filter through the vents above.

Some of the women coming aboard had been wearing man-made fibres. Lord only knew how sticky they must be feeling by now. Cotton was at least cool and unclinging. Everything she had with her was made from it. Not that she planned on wearing anything much beyond shorts and T-shirt during the day.

Noel came back to seize the microphone again, this time to announce that everything was in order. They should reach the hotel around five-thirty depending on traffic conditions, he finished. Dinner was from seven-thirty to nine-thirty, so they would all have plenty of time to settle in first.

Traffic conditions, Lynn discovered as soon as they left the airport vicinity were, to say the least, frenetic. Noel informed them that due to the sheer number of vehicles on the roads, private cars were only allowed into the city on certain days of the week in accordance with registration letters posted. He kept up a running commentary on points of interest as they progressed through this rather shabby part of the Greek capital, drawing their attention to far-off glimpses of the Parthenon between buildings. Like most others on the coach, Lynn attempted to get a snap, knowing full well that if it turned out at all it would be as a dot in the distance. She would recognise it for what it was if no one else did. That was all that mattered.

The road west followed the coastline for the most part, a wide highway bearing clear through to Patras at the far end of the Corinthian Gulf. Noel came back to sit with Lynn for a few minutes after the first toll gate, ignoring the glances directed their way from across the aisle.

'This bit doesn't have too much going for it,' he acknowledged, accurately reading her mind. 'Civilisation caught up. To see it at its best you have to take the old road right down by the sea, especially at this time of year when the flowers are out.'

'I'll remember that,' she said. 'It's worth knowing. The Amalia is Greek owned, isn't it?'

'All the way. As a matter of fact, the owner's there right now. The Stephanos chain stretches from Athens right down to Crete. One thing you should be prepared for. Greek 'A' class isn't quite the same thing as English 'A' class—not outside Athens, at any rate. The Amalia has only been opened five years so it's more up to date than most, but things still go wrong. The air-conditioning works when it feels like it, the lifts about the same. The food's good, though.'

'Thank heaven for that.' She gave him a quizzical look. 'Is it general policy to lower expectations this way?'

'Only for some,' he said, taking the question seriously. 'You look like someone used to only the best.'

'How deceptive of me.' Her tone was light. 'I'm sure I'll get by.'

'Anything you need just come to me,' he told her without batting an eyelid. 'That's what I'm here for.

Have to go now. Paper work to do. See you when we arrive.'

Lynn watched the passing scenery after that. On the coastal side of the highway there were occasional glimpses of small towns and fishing villages, with whitewashed cubist houses sparkling in the sunlight. The sea was a melting blue, edged in the distance by the ragged shoreline of the peninsula. To the right lay ever-steepening hillside, the lower slopes covered in wild flowers, trees lining the ridge above.

When they did finally reach the Canal it was quite suddenly, rounding a curve in the road to thunder and rattle their way across a great iron bridge. There were people lining the footpaths either side of the dual-carriageway, one and all peering into the depths. The sides rose vertically like yellow cliffs from a watery base so far below it looked almost too narrow to admit the ship already entering its seaward end.

Beyond the bridge, the coach made a sharp and hazardous left turn across the traffic stream to take a minor road running down through a settlement not unlike a motorway service station, with garages and cafés and even a supermarket. From here the road curved down between wooded slopes to the tiny port of Isthmia, before turning landwards once more through olive groves and vineyards where black goats wandered freely. Noel hadn't exaggerated, Lynn conceded. The landscape here looked untouched by the twentieth century, its coastal plain backed by rolling olive-coloured hills and barren crags already turning purple as the sun sank towards the west.

The coach that had followed them all the way from Athens turned off first, leaving them to continue southwards for another two or three miles before they reached their destination. The Amalia lay down a narrow, roughly paved road edged both sides by trees.

One cleared area held a typical Greek *taverna*, with tables and chairs set out beneath a huge canvas awning, the latter held erect at its outer edge by what looked like rusty iron tubing. A row of kerosene tins painted bright colours held a riot of geraniums.

Then they were pulling up before the hotel itself, necks stretching to view the long, low curve of grey stone which was to be their home for the coming two weeks.

Wide glass doors admitted the new arrivals to a lobby magnificently floored in terrazzo and running clear through the rear of the building, with a fine view through a frame of trees to the sea. There were sitting areas with comfortable leather armchairs, while a couple of wide steps gave access to a large open lounge with a pool and fountain as its centrepiece. Nice, Lynn approved, waiting her turn to check in at the desk where three clerks struggled manfully to sort out keys. Enough to explore without being too overpoweringly big.

Turning her head, she became aware of the man standing in a doorway to the rear of the desk watching the proceedings. The manager probably, she reflected. He looked too self-sufficient to be anything else. The black curly hair and dark eyes had to be Greek in origin, although he was taller than average, body muscular beneath the tailored shirt. Attractive, she supposed, if one liked the type. He had a good strong face, the bones clearly defined.

As if sensing her regard, he glanced in her direction, eyes suddenly narrowing a fraction. Refusing to be embarrassed by being caught out, Lynn held his gaze for several seconds before calmly turning her attention elsewhere, ignoring the faint twist of his lips. Let him think what he liked. She wasn't interested in him on any level beyond that of his calling. She had better things to do with her time than make a play for one of the staff.

He stayed where he was in the doorway the whole time she was waiting to claim her room, although she didn't look at him again. Key in one hand and suitcase in the other, she made her way over to the curving staircase. With a first-floor room there was going to be little need to use the lifts at all, which, judging from their limited capacity and considering the size of the place, wasn't going to be a bad thing. Porters were in short supply over here; she had already discovered that last autumn. Not that it worried her unduly. She was young enough and fit enough to carry her own bags.

Her room was simple to the point of being austere, but both it and the adjoining bathroom were spotlessly clean. There was a small balcony offering a magnificent view out over the gulf, narrowed this far inland to a few miles across. Tree-shaded gardens stretched out to the sea, with a swimming pool just visible off to the right. The beach, she already knew, was mostly pebble, but there were supposed to be plenty of little coves within walking distance for those who preferred sand. All in all a good choice to have made, she decided, returning indoors to unpack. If the food was as good as Noel had said then she had really struck lucky.

By seven-thirty she was showered and dressed in fine white cotton, her hair brushed loose to fall softly about her face. A few sessions at a solarium had coloured her legs sufficiently well to look good without stockings. With pale pink varnish on her toe nails to match that on her fingers, and a pair of slender-heeled sandals to complement her outfit, she felt ready to face the world.

The lobby was awash with people, not all of them

British. A party of young Italians filled the air with fast and seemingly furious sound as they discussed some item posted on the notice board close by the entrance. Lynn headed for the boutique and gift shop she could see in the lower section, browsing for a while through the racks of street and beachwear with no real intention of buying. Hotel shops were always more expensive than those in the local towns. Better to wait before plunging on anything, even if she did rather fancy one of the lovely embroidered cotton blouses.

The gift shop held her interest for only a short time because there was no one she had to buy for. It was going to be at least a month after she got back before she could manage her next visit home, which made the whole process of present buying pointless. Thinking about the last time brought a momentary frown. Caroline should come home and stop their parents worrying about her the way they did. The marriage was finished. Her letters had already made that clear. There was nothing to hold her in Toronto. Not anymore. Marrying a man only six weeks after meeting him had hardly been a wise move to start with, especially when it meant moving to another country. It hadn't taken her long to fall out of love with Reece and find someone else. He couldn't be blamed for refusing to take her back when the new romance fell through.

'If you're not going to buy that card, how about coming for a drink instead?' asked a voice, already familiar, at her elbow, startling her out of her thoughts. 'I just got through at the desk.'

Lynn turned to smile at the good-looking courier, slipping the postcard back into the stand as she did so. 'I was contemplating how many I'm going to need,' she said lightly. 'Tomorrow will do.'

'That answers part of the question,' he said. 'How about the rest?'

'You're allowed to pick out individuals from the crowd?' she prevaricated.

His grin was appealing. 'Once I'm off duty for the day I'm just another guy. A drink isn't going to break any rules, written or otherwise.'

She capitulated without further argument, aware that refusal would not only be discourteous but downright unfriendly into the bargain. 'All right. And thanks.'

The bar lay on the far side of the lounge, its sliding glass doors opening on to a wide terrace already well-occupied. It was easy to pick out the newcomers among the bunch by their relatively white skins, although the Latins had a head start anyway with their natural olive complexions.

'How many nationalities do they get coming here?' she asked Noel when he brought over their drinks to the seats she had chosen. 'There's a French couple in the room next to mine. I could hear them talking when I was out on the balcony.'

'Mostly French, Italian, and British,' he said, sitting down beside her. 'And a few Americans on occasion. Different arrival days, of course. It would be all hell let loose every week otherwise. The French come in on a Friday, the Italians on a Monday and us on a Wednesday. You're staying put the whole two weeks, I know, but some do a split between Corinth and Poros. Best of both worlds, I suppose.'

'I shan't exactly be staying put,' Lynn advised. 'I'm here to work.'

'Work?' He sounded surprised. 'First time I've had anyone even mention that word at this end of the holiday!' He paused, studying her with curiosity. 'What kind of work?'

'Research. I want to become a tour hostess with Treasury next season. They don't take on anyone under twenty-five.'

'They're the classical tour operators, aren't they?'

'That's right. Which means I have to know what I'm talking about when it comes to Greek antiquity. I spent the winter studying the subject at night-school. This fortnight I plan to tag along in the wake of some of the organised parties and listen to the presentation.'

'In that case, wouldn't you have been better off joining an actual tour?'

She smiled, shaking her head. 'The prices were outside my pocket. Even allowing for getting to and from the sites, I'll still be saving around a hundred and fifty.'

'And next winter?'

'More study, I suppose. I'm determined to get the job.'

'Good luck to you, then. Anyone prepared to devote that much time to a project deserves to get on. What do you do for a living now?'

She laughed. 'I take foreign visitors on guided tours of London.'

'Should stand you in good stead,' Noel commented. 'Does your family live in London?'

'No, Yorkshire. Richmond.'

'Nice place. I spent a night there on a walking holiday once.'

'It dies in winter. And there's a dearth of jobs. I left two years ago to seek fame and fortune in the big wide world. So far it's eluded me.'

Blue eyes regarded her admiringly. 'The big wide world doesn't know what it's missing.'

He was seated with his back to the bar. Laughing with him, Lynn found her attention drawn beyond him to the man in the pale cream suit talking to one of the waiters. The same man she had seen earlier in reception, and just as arrogantly sure of himself even from the rear. It was there in the very set of the dark head, the casual lifting of a foot to the raised plinth fronting the bar, the hand thrust into one trouser pocket.

He could see her looking at him through the mirrors lining the back wall, she realised suddenly. Even from here the sardonic quirk of a brow was all too evident. He finished his conversation with the waiter and sauntered away without so much as a glance in her direction, pausing here and there to acknowledge seated guests.

'You'd think he owned the place!' Lynn murmured, disgusted with herself for the colour she knew was tingeing her cheeks.

Noel twisted in his chair to follow her gaze. 'He does,' he said, turning back again. 'That's Andreas Stephanos.' He registered her sudden change of expression with obvious puzzlement. 'Something wrong?'

Lynn shook herself. She was being ridiculous. There must be hundreds of Greeks called Andreas. Caro's lover was domiciled in Toronto—at least she had assumed he was. The one letter she had received herself referring to the affair had given few actual details—not even a last name. It had been a surprise to hear from her at all, much less an intimate revelation. They had never been close the way sisters should be. The only possible reason was that Caro had needed an outlet and could find it nowhere else.

'Just a passing thought,' she said lightly. 'Nothing important. I think it's time I had something to eat.'

'I already ate.' Noel acknowledged. 'How about coming down to the disco later on?'

'I might.' It was far as she was prepared to commit

herself. She stood up, smoothing down her skirt over slender hips. 'Thanks for the drink, Noel. Sorry if I monopolised the conversation a bit, only you did ask.'

'Only because I genuinely wanted to know.' He had risen with her, lean and athletic in his navy slacks and shirt. 'Next time I'll tell you my life story. There's a meeting for today's arrivals at ten-thirty in the morning, by the way. I posted the notice on the board. You might be interested in some of the tours. We go to Olympia and Epidauros, among others. They're musts.'

'I'll have to work out my schedule,' she said. 'I'll be at the meeting anyway.'

He accompanied her to the door of the restaurant, handing her over to the *maitre d'* with an injunction to find her a good table. There were no placings for lone diners, Lynn realised as she followed the man the length of the already crowded room. Tables were set for four or six. He seated her with a family of three, giving her to understand that this would be her table for every meal except breakfast. It was necessary to keep some kind of order, she supposed, considering the groups constantly coming and going.

The others introduced themselves as Liz, Frank and Janet Downing from Chelmsford. The daughter was in her mid-teens, and pretty with it, her long fair hair caught back from her youthfully rounded face in a pony tail.

'I saw you with Noel in the bar,' she announced on a frankly envious note. 'He's really dishy!'

Her mother sighed and shook her head resignedly. 'I'm glad he's already taken.'

'He isn't taken,' Lynn denied without undue emphasis. 'We were only having a drink and a chat.' She looked back to the younger girl to add lightly, 'He's too old for you, anyway.'

'You sound just like my mother,' came the disgusted comment. 'I prefer older men.'

'That's enough from you, young lady,' said her father gruffly. 'You've far too much to say for yourself.'

'She's a real handful,' imparted his wife to Lynn, her expression appealing for sympathy. 'Boys, boys, boys, that's all she ever thinks about!'

If it were just boys, thought Lynn with a quirk of humour, there wouldn't be as much to worry about. She caught Janet's eye, recognising the flash of resentment. There had been times at sixteen or so when she had felt much the same way over parental attempts to lay down rules and regulations, although hers, in retrospect, had been a deal more sensitive about it than these two. In all likelihood, Janet was playing them up deliberately.

She continued to do so throughout the meal, which was a set menu but excellent in both quality and quantity. Their waiter was named Stavros, a typical Greek with his dark eyes and hair, his stocky build. In his early twenties, he spoke little English, but managed to communicate quite well in spite of it. Lynn refrained from addressing him in Greek herself, afraid that it might be construed as showing-off. She wasn't all that fluent anyway. Not yet. Another winter would make all the difference.

Every table on the terrace was occupied when she finally stepped out into the warm, sub-tropical night. The gardens were floodlit, leaving areas of shadow where the trees grew more closely together. Lynn found a narrow path and followed it through to a small paved area overlooking a scrap of cove, leaning on the rail to breathe deeply of the soft air and listen to the continuous high-pitched chirping of the cicadas. There was a smell, faint and emotive, of eucalyptus, and another she thought might be wild thyme. The moon spread a rippling path of silver across the wide expanse of sea, stopping short of the dark line of hills on the horizon. Over there was Epidauros, where lay the best preserved amphitheatre in the whole of Greece. Tomorrow she would start making the necessary arrangements. If she spent this first week concentrating on the Peloponnese area she could afford to devote the second week to Athens and points east.

'Avoiding the crowds or planning on meeting someone?' asked a mocking voice from over on her left, and she turned sharply to where a pale-suited figure lounged negligently against a tree trunk a few yards away. He hadn't been there when she arrived, she was certain—or almost certain. The trees here grew close in, forming a semi-circle about the viewing area. Forming privacy, too, she realised. She had wandered quite a way from the terrace and its population.

'Just enjoying the night,' she said. 'Are you a guest here, too?'

'Not exactly.' He moved then, coming out from the shadows into the moonlight so that she saw his face clearly for the first time. 'I didn't think it made any difference.'

Lynn stood her ground as he approached, feeling the antagonism rising sharply in her, mingled with some other emotion not yet fully defined. Andreas Sephanos spoke English with a distinct American accent. That had to be unusual in itself.

'I'm not sure what that's supposed to mean,' she said.

He came to a halt a couple of feet away, leaning an elbow on the rail as he looked at her, his mouth slanting. 'Moonlight suits you. Your hair looks silver.' One lean brown hand came out to touch the strand that curved her right cheek, smoothing it lightly downwards. Lynn jerked her head away involuntarily, lips compressing.

'Just get to the point. I'm sure there is one.'

'You're right.' He was smiling, the jeer unconcealed. 'The point is I know your type. You home in on the best prospect going. Your courier can hardly be more than a stop-gap. Even if he had the time I doubt if he'd have the funds.'

She was silent for a moment, struck dumb by the man's sheer nerve. When she did find her voice she had to make an effort to stop it from trembling with anger. 'You think I followed you down here?'

'You were only a couple of minutes behind me. Very few find their way along that path. That's why I like it.'

'And you're welcome to it!' She started to move away, desisting only when he put out a hand again to grasp her wrist.

'Don't run away. I didn't say I was unwilling to play. Just so long as we both know how we stand.'

'I know exactly how *I* stand,' she flashed. 'Get out of my way!'

He laughed. 'The chased becomes the chaser. All right, I'll go along. Run and I'll catch you. It's all part of the game.'

Lynn had never slapped a man across the face in her life but she did it now, finding a fierce exultation in the sharp crack of palm across cheek. She saw the sudden devilish light spring in the dark eyes, and the next instant was in his arms with his mouth on hers and the breath crushed from her by the hard strength of his body. In those few moments she was conscious of so many sensations, not least among them a sudden surging heat that started deep in the pit of her stomach. There was no brutality in the kiss, just a demand that allowed no quarter, searching, taking;

drawing an involuntary response. When he finally let her go she was insufficiently in command of herself to say or do a thing for several seconds.

'Now we each of us have the measure of the other,' he said softly. 'It should be an interesting relationship.'

Her breathing was ragged still but she had to make the effort. 'You can look for your entertainment elsewhere,' she got out in Greek, and had the satisfaction of seeing his eyes widen in surprise.

'A fair accent, too!'

The mockery found its mark. She reverted to English to add scathingly. 'Better than your Yankee one, at any rate!'

'I was educated in Canada.' He sounded amused. 'There's a subtle difference. Going already? The night only just got started.'

She had to get away, Lynn told herself, or she was going to blurt out something she might be sorry for afterwards. It was sheer coincidence. It *had* to be coincidence!

He made no attempt to stop her leaving, but she could feel him watching her until the trees hid her from sight. It was only a little after ten o'clock when she reached the terrace. There were less people there now; she could hear the sound of music from the direction of the open-air disco. Noel had said he would be there, but he was the last person she wanted to see right now. She needed to collect herself before she saw anyone.

It was quiet enough in her room with the balcony doors closed, but much too warm. The air vent was giving off the sound of a compressor and that was about all. Undressing, she went out onto the balcony in her thin cotton wrap, preferring the muted blare of music to the built-up heat of the day. There was no breeze, yet the air was delightfully cool on her skin. She felt she could sit out here all night just looking at the stars and the sea.

Stopping her thoughts from dwelling on the events of the last hour was impossible, of course. She could still feel the imprint of that man's lips. Educated in Canada, he had said. If he was now in his early thirties as he appeared to be, his education would have been completed ten years or more ago. Yes, but would he have retained the accent to such a degree if he'd been back here in Greece that length of time? Lynn doubted it. Which left her where? Caro's affair had ended six months ago when the man had walked out on her, that was all she had said. There had been no mention of his returning to his homeland.

She was going around in circles, she acknowledged wearily. Short of asking him outright, she was hardly likely to learn much more than she already knew. Unless Noel could tell her. It was worth a try. Anything rather than suffer a whole two weeks of doubt.

And if the unlikely should turn out to be the truth, what then? asked the small voice of reason. There was nothing she could say or do that would make any difference to a man like Andreas Stephanos. His kind of cynicism was inbred. The best thing she could do was steer clear of him altogether.

CHAPTER TWO

THE orientation talk took place in the television room with Noel perched on a high chair in the middle of the circle.

From describing the hotel and local facilities in some detail, he went on to talk about the various tours, wetting the cultural appetite with a series of word pictures designed to be irresistible. That was his job, of course, Lynn conceded. He would be paid a commission on all reservations made. The only one she herself was really tempted to consider was the day-long cruise to three of the nearer islands from Piraeus.

Noel signalled to her to wait for him as he gathered up his files at the end of the session, coming across to where she stood at the door with the whole bundle tucked precariously under an arm.

'Couldn't find my briefcase this morning,' he said. 'I had to root out my old sheets. Where did you get to last night?'

'I was in bed by ten-thirty,' she admitted. 'Well, ready for bed, at least.' She laughed. 'I must be getting old before my time!'

'Travelling makes me that way, too,' he said. 'Especially by plane. Have you decided on any tours yet? I need to know by this afternoon.'

'Just the Tuesday one to the islands for me. The final Tuesday. I can change a cheque and let you have the money now if you like.'

'Only if it's convenient.' He sounded disappointed. 'I was hoping to show you a few of the sights myself.'

'You wouldn't have time anyway,' she pointed out

24

on a practical note. 'Just keeping a whole coachload together and happy must be more than enough.'

'Surprising what you can fit in with a little prior planning. You wouldn't change your mind and come to the *Son et Lumière* tonight?'

Lynn shook her head. 'I'd rather visit Athens during the day and under my own steam.'

He accepted the refusal with good grace. 'All right then, so come and have a coffee with me now. I've half an hour to spare before I have to round up my group for the Canal trip.'

They took the coffee out on the terrace. Lynn made sure that this time the conversation centred on Noel rather than herself. He was twenty-seven, it turned out, and had been in this job for the past four years, changing locations every season. His home was in Cambridge, although his degree in Sociology had been obtained at Leicester.

'My "A" levels weren't good enough to make either of the big two,' he admitted cheerfully. 'I flunked a couple of subjects. I fancied going over to the States for a spell, but there was nothing doing.'

It was an opening and she grasped it, voice casual. 'Talking of the States, I heard this Stephanos man speaking English to someone last night. He has a real American accent.'

'Canadian,' Noel corrected. 'Sounds strange coming from him, doesn't it? I was intrigued enough to ask him about it. Seems he lived over there for about fifteen years until his father died suddenly in November last year and left him the whole caboodle. Don't ask me the whys and wherefores. He's not all that forthcoming when it comes down to the details. He's no newcomer to the hotel business, that's for sure. The staff have been on their toes since he arrived. Apparently he did a quick flip round the whole chain when he took over, then started again at the beginning to spend time ironing out the problems, if any. The Hellas in Athens is the flagship of the group. He came on here about a month ago.'

'Does he live in the hotel itself?' asked Lynn, still striving to sound only mildly interested.

'He has a suite on the top floor.' He cast a glance at his watch and pulled a face. 'Afraid I'm going to have to leave you. Duty calls. What do you have planned for tomorrow?'

'Olympia and Messene,' she said. 'Although I still have to arrange transport.'

'Try asking Theonassis at the desk. His brother drives a taxi. You'll get a fair deal.'

'Thanks.' She was grateful for the help. 'What about the money I owe you?'

'It will do later. I'll put you down anyway.' He was already on his feet, lifting a hand in farewell. 'See you.'

Lynn sat for a moment or two after he had gone, turning over the information he had imparted in her mind. It wasn't totally conclusive—not yet. But the chances were infinitely likely. Unbelievable coincidence maybe, yet it did happen.

The question was still the same. Even if this Andreas Stephenos did indeed prove to be the same man who had led her sister astray, what was she going to do about it? Caro was twenty-seven years old, not an innocent teenager. She had known what she was doing—the risks she was taking with her marriage. *He swept me off my feet*, she had claimed extravagantly in that one impassioned letter whilst still in the first throes of betrayal. *I gave him everything and he threw it back in my face. I'll never love another man the way I loved Andreas.* The last Lynn could take with a pinch of salt. Caro's emotions had never run that deep. All the same, she had not emerged unscarred from the encounter.

It was a problem she had to shelve in the end, because there seemed no answer. Regardless of how she felt about a man of Andreas Stephanos' type, there was little redress to be had against him.

Having arranged through the man on duty at the desk to meet his brother that evening and arrange a price for the following day's hire, Lynn spent the rest of the morning exploring the hotel and its immediate environs. Lunch was a buffet affair with a mixture of Greek and English dishes to choose from. She had a Greek salad, enjoying the strong flavour of the feta cheese, finishing off with a ripe peach peeled for safety and sliced into succulent quarters. She was the only person sitting alone but she refused to feel lonely. Striking up friendships of any kind could only complicate matters. She was going to need all the time at her disposal.

Later, carrying all she might conceivably need in a pink nylon sling bag, she set out from the hotel beach in search of somewhere a little more secluded in order to do some serious reading. The cove adjoining theirs was wider and sandier and empty of life at the moment, but with a regular campsite visible under the fringing trees it was hardly likely to remain so for long. Lynn scrambled across the rocks on the far side and continued her search, splashing through pools in happy disregard of the cheap beach shoes she had bought from the shop earlier. The heat was intense, and likely to remain so for at least another couple of hours. Shade of some kind was going to be an essential factor, she acknowledged, and soon. Already she could feel the skin on her exposed shoulders starting to tingle a little.

She found what she was looking for in the shape of a

small headland, which curved towards its seaward end to form a natural pool edged by a great slab of white rock with the overhang behind creating partial shade. The gently lapping water was crystal clear, the fine sandy base a background for a host of tiny fish. Lynn parked her bag and peeled off her shorts and T-shirt to reveal the brief blue-and-white bikini underneath, hesitating for only a second before removing the top half. Back there at the hotel most of the women had been topless, both in the sea and out of it, and regardless of age. Here in private there was no initial self-consciousness to overcome; nothing but the sheer delight of being unrestricted by straps and clips.

The water was deep enough for diving. She went in with scarcely a splash, surfacing to smooth her hair from her face and revel in the feel of the liquid silk on her heated skin. It was bliss, sheer bliss! She dived again, kicking up a clean pair of heels in an excess of zeal and running her fingers into the silver sand below. There was so much life down here, so many minute creatures. A starfish crept with infinite slowness across a spur of rock, all five arms gently pulsing. Lynn touched it with the tip of a finger, surprised by its lack of reaction.

Coming up for air, she knuckled the water from her eyes then reached up both hands to squeeze her hair while using her legs to keep herself afloat. The sight of the man sitting on the rock she had so recently vacated was enough of a shock in itself before she realised who he was.

'A regular mermaid!' he mocked. 'Don't let me interrupt the display. I'm quite content to watch.'

In water this clear there was little point in attempting to disguise the fact that she was wearing so little. As if to emphasise it, Andreas lifted a negligent hand to show the bikini top dangling from his fingers.

'You forgot something,' he said.

It was on the tip of her tongue to ask him to throw the garment to her, but she desisted. That kind of game would no doubt be right up his street. No way was he going to make her reveal embarrassment. Hers wouldn't be the first bare breasts he had seen. Not by a long chalk! Setting her teeth, she swam the few yards to the edge of the pool, only then realising how nearly impossible it was going to be to pull herself out of the water at this particular point.

'First look before you leap,' he quoted, watching her sardonically. 'Would you like a hand?'

'Not from you,' she retorted, losing sight of her aim in the heat of the moment. 'I'll find my own way out!'

She did eventually, pausing on the rocky shelf to regain her breath before attempting to stand up. The pool was no real trap because the way was open to the sea, but the advice, though ill-founded, had been appropriate enough. After this she would certainly be looking first.

Andreas watched her coming without stirring from his seat on a jutting spur. He was wearing white shorts and a tight-fitting cotton T-shirt, the latter revealing well-defined muscle in shoulders and biceps. His forearms were lean and strong like his legs, the olive skin lightly covered in dark hair. Lynn nerved herself to hold out a hand for the bikini top.

'I'll have my property if you don't mind.'

He ran a deliberate eye over her slender curves, lingering with intent on firmly rounded, pink-tipped breasts, before sliding on and down over the flatness of her stomach to long and shapely legs. Lynn was conscious of the brevity of the single garment she wore, of the faint tremor in her thighs due to tension as she forced herself to stand still under his scrutiny. Let him look! She had nothing to be ashamed of.

'I do mind,' he said. 'I prefer you this way. Any woman who chooses to strip is looking for attention.'

Green eyes flashed resentment. 'I was under the impression I had privacy!'

'On a public beach? Anyone may walk along here. Some might even regard it as an open invitation.'

'Not everyone has your kind of mind,' she came back scathingly. 'Didn't last night teach you *any*thing?'

'It taught me not to underestimate your basic knowhow. The best way to attract a man is to keep him guessing.'

She studied him suspiciously. 'Did you follow me here?'

Dark eyes taunted. 'How else would I have known where you were?' He stood up slowly, smiling as she took an involuntary step backwards. 'Don't overplay the act. You want it as much as I do.'

'Don't you dare speak to me like that!' she spluttered, feeling immediately ridiculous because the words themselves were so trite. 'There's nothing *you* could offer me that I'd want,' she tagged on, curling a lip. 'So just take your Greek-Canadian technique and get out of here, *kyrie*. It's strictly second-rate so far as I'm concerned!'

'Tell me no in Greek,' he mocked, undeterred in his advance. 'Not that it's going to make any difference because I still shan't believe it.'

Lynn came up against rock, unable to retreat any further. How the devil did she get through to him? she wondered frantically, searching the hard-boned features. He was bigger than she, and certainly a great deal stronger. Complaining of rape in a strange country was one thing, proving it another. This Greek cynic had the weight of his nationality behind him. Who was going to take her word against his?

The hands coming up to curve her waist were purposeful, holding her still as he bent his head. Lynn tried to keep her lips sealed against him, but he nuzzled them open, tasting the inner softness. His hands moved again to cup both breasts, the balls of his thumbs stroking roughly across her nipples while she writhed to his touch. She could feel the flesh peaking, and could do nothing to stop it.

Pressurised by his hardness, her thighs parted a little, accommodating the angles of his body with an intimacy that sent tremor after tremor racing through her. Her insides had turned to liquid, like molten fire reaching down to every extremity. It wouldn't be rape, came the stray thought, plucked from the inner recesses of her mind. She actually wanted this man. That acknowledgement, anathema as it was, gave her the physical strength she needed to push him away from her.

'Leave me alone!' she spat out. 'Just leave me alone!'

He did so with surprising readiness, standing back to view her flushed cheeks and blazing eyes with grim humour. 'Never let it be said I took an unwilling woman! Are you punishing me or yourself?'

'I'm asking you to stop treating me like a tramp, that's all,' she got out. 'You don't have the right.'

He was silent for a long moment considering her, his breathing still roughened. 'I'm not concerned with rights,' he said at length, 'only dues.'

'On the premise that any female travelling alone deserves all she gets?' Her chin was up, her tone scornful. 'That'a a sexist theory if ever I heard one!'

'We're a sexist race. You might do well to remember it.' He bent and picked up the bikini top he had dropped on the rock before grabbing her, holding it out to her. 'Cover yourself.'

She did so with fingers that trembled, the anger still

surging inside her. She was wrong about him. She had to be wrong! Caro would no more have been drawn to a man of his kind that she was herself. Her mind shied away from the memory of those few brief moments of near surrender. It wouldn't be happening again, that was for sure. She didn't want him anywhere near her!

He was moving away when she looked up again, climbing the low ridge to head for the shore without a backward glance. Already dried off in the sun, Lynn spread her towel and got out her book, but the printed lines made little sense to a mind still seething. Eventually she gave it up and sat with arms clasped about bent knees gazing out to sea. It was probably a good thing she was going to be spending so little time at the Amalia over the coming days because it cut down the chances of another encounter with the obnoxious Greek. If she wanted to get anywhere at all with her studies she had to put him out of her mind.

It was going to be easier said than done.

A stiff breeze blew up around three-thirty, turning the sea from near flat calm to rolling, white-capped waves. Awakened from a doze by the spray breaking across the rock, Lynn retreated swiftly to dry land and made her way back to the hotel to have tea on the sundeck.

There was people in the sea despite the breakers. The two older couples who had been on the coach yesterday were having themselves a whale of a time surfing without the benefit of boards. Watching them, Lynn hoped she would have as much energy left when she was that age. One needed a companion for that sort of fun, she acknowledged a little ruefully. Male or female didn't matter, providing there was someone to shout to, to wave one's arms at, to be generally exuberant with.

The breeze had dropped again by evening. Lynn

went in late to dinner in the hope of missing the Downings, whose family differences were already becoming a pain. It was Stavros' day off, it appeared. Faced with the bold eyes and Adonis-like features of his stand-in, Stamàtis, Lynn confined her attention strictly to her food, but to little avail.

He would be off duty at ten o'clock, he confided when serving dessert. By that time the display of Greek dancing would be over and the disco about to begin. Would she meet him there? Lynn murmured some excuse about having an early night and made her escape as soon as she could, aware that her admirer was in no way put off by her refusal. Tenacity was the name of the game.

The display was scheduled to begin at nine according to the notice board in the lobby. Lynn got there at ten minutes to the hour to find every table taken except for one right on the edge of the dance floor itself, which everyone seemed to be avoiding.

Reserved for *Kyrios* Stephanos and his party, one of the waiters advised in answer to her query. They would be here any moment. They arrived as Lynn was settling herself down on a lone chair wedged to one side of a pillar supporting the vine-clad loggia which housed the bar, ushered through the throng with all the deference due to the owner of the hotel.

Andreas was wearing another of the superbly cut, lightweight suits, his dark brown shirt open at the throat. His guests numbered four, consisting of a couple in their thirties, together with a boy around eight years of age and a young woman Lynn thought might be a nanny or governess judging from the way in which she saw the child seated and comfortable before slipping into her own chair. The older woman was beautiful, her features finely cut and regular beneath the cloud of dark hair. She seemed to take little note of the man on her right who was most likely her husband, concentrating all her attention on Andreas as he bent his head to hear what she was saying.

Registering the intimate manner in which her red-tipped hand rested on his sleeve and the provocative smile on her lips, Lynn wondered cynically if his professed disapproval of predatory women extended itself only to foreigners. Certainly he was making no objection.

The Greek dancers were all male, and took their task very seriously. A little disappointed at first that the music was taped, Lynn soon lost herself in the intricate footwork and the grace and agility of these young men as they performed the various movements. An invitation for members of the audience to join in one of the better known numbers met with slow response at first. Drawn to her feet by one of the troupe who spoke no English and refused to recognise her reluctance, she gave in to the good-natured urgings of those about her and allowed herself to be included in the gathering, avoiding so much as a glance in the direction of the table where Andreas and his guests still sat watching the proceedings.

Nothing about the dance they were shown was difficult, although some made heavy weather of it. It didn't matter, Lynn conceded, following the simple steps demonstrated by the three Greeks in the centre of the circle. The whole idea was to have fun trying. She gave herself over to doing just that, laughing along with the rest when the music speeded up and they all began to fall over their own feet, finishing up eventually in a breathless, giggling heap.

'That was sure somethin'!' exclaimed the big hearty man wearing tartan trousers who had been on Lynn's right hand. 'Hope Betty got a couple of good

snaps to show the folks back home!' He glanced down
at Lynn as they began to move off the floor to return
to their respective seats. 'You're on your own, aren't
you? That's a real pity. How about coming across and
having a drink with me and the good lady? We're only
here for the one night. Doing the museums with
Treasury Tours.' His grimace was semi-serious.
'Betty's idea. Thought we ought to get ourselves some
culture while we're doing Europe. She spotted you
sitting over there a while back. Thought you looked
lonely. Always wanting to help people is Betty.' The
last with fondness. He cast her a glance. 'Not leaving
yet, are you?'

'No,' Lynn admitted, smiling at him. 'And yes, I'd
love to have a drink with you.'

'Great! We can pick up another chair now the
crowd's thinning out.'

Betty turned out to be a well-preserved American
matron with beautifully dressed grey hair and a pair of
the kindliest eyes Lynn had seen in ages. They were
taking this tour because it was something she had
always wanted to do, she confided comfortably when
they were settled with glasses in front of them. Later
they were moving on to Austria and France before
heading across the channel to do Britain in the final
three days of the vacation.

'Fred's more for sitting on his ass back home now
he's retired,' she added without rancour. 'But I told
him he can do that anytime. We couldn't have
afforded this trip when we were younger so it was now
or never. The things we've seen they're not going to
believe back home! More than two thousand years old,
some of these ruins. Did you know that?'

'I'm learning about it,' Lynn told her. 'As a matter
of fact, I'm hoping to be doing the self-same tour next
year as a courier.'

'You don't say!' The tone was gratifyingly reverential. 'Well, now, you must be a real clever young lady!'

Lynn laughed. 'I haven't got the job yet. Which part of America are you from?'

'Little town midwest called Wellsburg,' said Fred. 'Leastways, Betty is. I've only been naturalised thirty-odd years. I'm Toronto born and bred.' He took a deep pull at his lager, wiping the froth from his mouth with the back of a huge hand. 'I got talking earlier on to the guy sitting back there at that table they were saving. Seems he spent some time in my home town. Even sounds Canadian. Real odd coming from a Greek. I'd like to have had more time with him.'

Lynn felt odd herself, not really sure of her emotions. It was the final piece of evidence she needed, the connection that could feasibly no longer be in doubt. Andreas Stephanos and her sister's lover were one and the same man. That sensual mouth had kissed Caro's lips, his hands caressed her body; they had lain together naked, entwined, whispering words of love. She didn't want to think about it yet the pictures kept coming.

'Those folks with him are leaving,' Betty observed. 'He's not going with them either. Why don't you ask him over for another chat?'

Over my dead body, Lynn thought, but it was already too late because Fred was on his feet and calling across the heads of those in between the two tables, 'Hey, there! Come and join us. Like to buy you a drink!'

In the following moment Lynn couldn't be sure what the response had been because she had her back to the dance floor. Only when Fred started forward to extend a friendly hand did she realise that Andreas had accepted the invitation.

'Getting to be quite a party,' exclaimed the American with jovial gratification as the younger man slid his length into the newly procured chair. 'This young lady is English, from London. Name of Lynn. Afraid I didn't get yours earlier.'

Black eyes met green, the former alight with familiar mockery. 'Lynn will tell you,' he said. 'We already met.'

'Andreas Stephanos,' she intoned clearly, refusing to be the first to look away. 'He owns the place. Not only this hotel, as a matter of fact, but four or five others like it.'

'You don't say!' Betty's voice held the exact same note it had held a few minutes ago on the same comment. 'A Greek tycoon!'

'A relatively minor one,' he assured her drily. Without turning his head, he lifted one lean brown hand and snapped his fingers, the sound carrying even above the beat of taped pop music. 'Drinks are on the house. What would you like?'

A waiter appeared as if from nowhere, shooting away again as soon as he had the order. Everyone was on their toes because the big boss was here. Lynn hoped he was properly impressed. She had considered refusing to drink with him, and rejected the idea because Fred and Betty deserved better than to be embroiled in a private affair.

Affair? She wanted suddenly to laugh. That was the very *last* thing she would want with this man!

'I hope you're enjoying your evening,' he said now, addressing the three of them as a group rather than individuals. 'This kind of music isn't everyone's ideal, but we have to cater for the young as well as the mature.'

Betty's eyes were twinkling. 'That's a real sensitive way of putting it.'

'The Greeks are a sensitive race.' Lynn spoke lightly; the glance she directed was anything but. 'Isn't that right, *kyrie?*'

'A moment ago you called me Andreas,' he returned, ignoring the challenge. 'Don't go formal on me now.'

Fred laughed, shaking his head. 'You know, I still can't take in that accent coming from you! How long were you in Canada anyway?'

'Fifteen years, apart from the odd visit back here from time to time.'

'Your family emigrate, or what?'

'I was sent out to complete my education.'

'That surely didn't take fifteen years.'

The dark eyes were beginning to show faint signs of impatience, but he answered civilly enough. 'I went on to take hotel management. Later I was offered a job and decided to stay. I came home to Greece when my father died last year.'

The potted history had only gone part way towards satisfying the other man's curiosity, that was evident from his expression. It was only the arrival of the waiter with their drinks that stopped him from voicing further questions. Andreas lifted his glass of Metaxa brandy in smiling salute to the three of them. '*Yassu!*'

A sudden lull in background sound signalled the end of a tape. When the music started again it was slower, designed to appeal to the traditional element. Several couples took to the floor immediately, making the most of the opportunity to be close for a change. Andreas put down his glass and got to his feet.

'You won't mind if I take Lynn away from you for a few minutes?' he enquired courteously of the older couple. 'It's been a long time since I danced.'

'Go right ahead.' Betty looked as pleased as if she herself had engineered the invitation. 'Enjoy yourselves!'

Only then did he glance in Lynn's direction, one brow lifting. 'You're not too tired?'

Once again she could find no way of putting him down without involving the others. Seething, her smile fixed, she rose to join him, steeling herself for the touch of those long fingers under her elbow as he steered her towards the floor. The glint in his eyes when he drew her to him did nothing to appease her anger.

'I don't like being put on the spot that way,' she hissed. 'Why don't you just disappear!'

'In a puff of smoke?' He shook his head, openly amused by her fury. 'Not my style.'

'You could always slither down the nearest crack,' she retorted, and felt his hand tighten at her back.

'Not very nice,' he said. 'Not very nice at all. I might have to teach you some manners before we're through.'

'What's never started can't be finished,' she came back smartly. 'Contrary to your own inflated opinion, *kyrie*, you're not irresistible!'

'But tempting?' He was looking at her mouth, watching the faint quiver of her lower lip, voice suddenly softer, almost a caress in itself. 'The way I'm tempted. You're here for two weeks, aren't you?'

The switch in attitude took her breath away for a moment. When she did find her voice again it was with scarcely controlled venom. 'If I were here for a year it would make no difference! I'm not available. Can't you get that through your head? I don't have any interest in acquiring myself a meal ticket for the duration!'

'So I made a mistake. I apologise. You reminded me . . .' He broke off abruptly, shrugging broad shoulders. 'It isn't important. We can begin again, can't we?'

She had reminded him of Caro, that was what he

had been going to say, if not in as many words. From which she deduced what? He had been the one to walk out on the relationship, not the other way round. He was the one who should be made to suffer.

And what better way to do it than through his male pride? came the sudden notion. He had presented her with the perfect opportunity. Leading on a man of his type could be dangerous, but she was capable of handling it. She would make herself capable.

The resolve lasted bare seconds before common sense reasserted itself. She had more important matters to think about than leading this man a dance, Lynn acknowledged. Much as she felt he deserved it, she would have to pass.

'There wouldn't be much point in beginning anything,' she said coolly. 'I don't plan on spending a great deal of time at the Amalia from tomorrow. There's too much else to see.'

He looked at her for a moment as if weighing up her sincerity. 'You're taking the organised tours?'

'No, I'll either be hiring taxis by the day or using local transport.'

'It's still going to cost you.'

'I've allowed for it.'

'I could drive you where you wanted to go,' he offered surprisingly. 'Maybe not every day, but certainly some of them.'

Lynn gazed at him, taken aback. 'Why would you go to that trouble?' she asked at length.

'I told you. I'd like to spend some time with you.' He was smiling. 'We speak the same language, you and I.'

Like hell! she thought. Aloud she said with irony, 'And what would be *your price?*'

He laughed. 'It's flexible. No more than you want to give.'

She could feel her pulses quickening, the rising temptation. 'Is that a promise?'

'I don't go back on my word,' he said. 'It's agreed then?'

'I already booked for tomorrow,' she prevaricated, still not wholly swayed.

'I'm tied up all morning anyway, but I'll make sure the whole of Saturday is free.' He wasn't about to let her off the hook. 'You'll be back for the evening?'

'Yes, but . . .'

'We'll have dinner together in my rooms.'

The tempo had altered again, this time to a rumba rhythm. Lynn moved back so that their bodies were no longer touching, hips swaying in accord. 'That's going a little too fast,' she said smoothly. 'I'll have the dinner I've already paid for thanks.'

His shrug was philosophical. 'It's your choice. You wouldn't deny me the chance to show you some real Greek dancing?'

'Tonight's wasn't it?'

He shook his head. 'Tonight was for tourists. This whole set-up is geared to the tourists. The majority wouldn't appreciate the subtler side of our culture.'

'You're so sure I would?'

'I think so.' His tone had softened again, sensual in its intonation. 'I think there's a whole lot more to you than meets the eye.'

More than he even suspected, she thought with cynicism. But he was going to find out.

CHAPTER THREE

'You looked good together,' Betty told them on their return to the table. 'You certainly can do the Latin stuff!'

'And neither of us are Latins,' Andreas responded mildly. He drained his glass, setting it down again with a faint thud. 'Afraid I'm going to have to leave you. I have some telephone calls to make. Feel free to order what you want.'

Lynn met the dark eyes as he got to his feet, registering the silent message. She murmured a reply to his general farewell, conscious of the unconcealed disappointment in Betty's face as he walked away.

'I thought you'd made a hit there,' said the latter frankly, the moment he was out of earshot. 'He's really something, that guy!'

'Isn't he?' Lynn was smiling, not about to give anything away. 'I expect he can pick and choose when it comes to girls. There are enough here.'

'He'd have a hard time finding another one with the same looks and brains,' came the ready reply. 'You sell yourself short, honey!'

Not this time, Lynn reflected hardily. One way or another, *Kyrios* Stephanos was going to get his comeuppance.

It was almost midnight before she finally took her leave, wishing the pair of them all the best for the rest of their vacation.

'Look us up if you ever get over to the States,' Betty urged, passing across the address she had scribbled on a page torn from a diary. 'We'd love to see you!'

'I will,' she promised. 'Anyway, you're going to take one of my tours when you get to London, remember?'

'You bet,' said Fred. 'Looking forward to it.'

She left them still watching the dancers, and made her way back to the main building. The breeze had died at sunset, leaving a night so still the tree tops looked as if they had been etched against the starlit sky. Lynn lingered for a moment or two on the terrace before going indoors, reluctant to face the comparative heat of her room. Something should be done about the air-conditioning, although if the compressor was worn out it was doubtful if any improvement could be made during the coming two weeks. A word in Andreas' ear might not go amiss. She may as well take some advantage of their association, if only for the sake of those still to visit the Amalia in future months. July and August must be stinking hot in this part of the world.

Theonassis was still on duty at the desk. He seemed to work all hours. He raised a hand in respectful greeting as she moved towards the stairs. Earlier, before dinner, she had arranged for an eight o'clock start with his brother Peter, planning to take breakfast as soon as the restaurant opened at seven-thirty. It was going to be a long day, and a tiring one. There was even a chance she might feel like crying off the planned evening. Andreas wouldn't like it, but why should she care? He deserved little consideration. It might even serve a purpose to appear reluctant. Wasn't it he himself who had said that the best way to attract a man was to keep him guessing?

Regardless, she found her thoughts dwelling on him as she prepared for bed, recalling the look in his dark eyes, the feel of his arms when he held her. Planning to take him for a ride was all very well, only she was going to have to make very sure she retained control of the situation. He was too insidiously attractive—too much the total male. It wasn't going to be easy to stay inviolate, but she could do it. For Caro, she told herself. Her own sister merited no less than a total effort.

She was up at first light, watching the sun rise on a sea tinged with pink silver. Way out on the horizon a ship stood towards the Canal, its hull gleaming white as the rays caught it. Even as she looked, sea and sky turned deep blue, merging at the edges into one great curving bowl.

A dog barked somewhere among the small village of villas behind the hotel grounds, and was mercifully silent again. Lynn went back indoors to find a swimsuit and a towel. An early morning swim would set her up for the day to come. At this hour she was likely to have the pool to herself.

The lobby appeared deserted, although she could hear sounds coming from the direction of the restaurant. Outside the air felt like wine, laden with scent from a dozen sources. Slipping down the steps to the pool deck, she was momentarily disconcerted to find it already occupied, until she realised who the man was. Noel lifted a hand in smiling recognition and swam across to where she stood on the edge, resting his elbows to support his weight on it as he looked up at her.

'Another early bird! I usually have it all to myself this time of day.'

'I could leave you to it,' she offered.

'No way,' he said predictably. 'It's probably going to be the only chance I have to talk to you before tonight. We're off to Delphi at seven. I have a free evening after I've manned the desk for the usual couple of hours. I thought we might have a drink in Corinth by way of a change.'

'You have your own transport?' Lynn queried, playing for time.

'No, I use taxis to get around. They're cheap, and pretty reliable.' He cocked an eyebrow. 'How about it?'

She smiled, casting discretion to the winds. 'I'd like it. Move over, I'm coming in.'

They left the pool together, chatting amicably as they went back indoors. The opened restaurant doors revealed a fair number of people already seated. A six-thirty breakfast for those going on the tour, Lynn remembered. Delphi was a four-hour journey each way, though probably less by car. She would probably have been better splitting her base between here and Athens, except that she had been unable to find an operator offering that particular deal. Still, if Andreas took her it would cut down on expenses. She wondered idly if the Jaguar parked in one of the spaces close by the main doors was his. A regular status symbol in this part of the world no doubt.

'I'd better look snappy,' said Noel, viewing the time. 'I'm supposed to be sitting there ready and waiting on the coach when they emerge. I'll walk up with you. I'm on the same floor.'

'You've already had breakfast?' Lynn queried as they mounted the stairs.

'Never eat it on tour days. Just a cup of coffee.' He paused on the landing, indicating left. 'I go this way. See you after dinner then?'

'Fine.' She gave him a smile. 'Have a nice day!'

The coach was long gone when she herself got outside at eight. The young Greek who was to be her driver for the day was already waiting by the side of his Vauxhall saloon. Lynn elected to sit up in front rather than in the back, not only because it seemed friendlier but because she could see more. Peter was intrigued by her insistence on speaking his language, obviously unaccustomed to foreigners who could offer more than the few simple words imparted by the various couriers. Before they had gone very far Lynn found herself telling him her real reason for being here in Greece, hearing in turn how it was his own ambition to come to England in order to join another brother already there. As a native of a Common Market country, there was nothing to stop him except money. One more year of taxi-driving, he told her, and he would have enough saved to buy a small share in his brother's restaurant business.

They took the Patras highway as far as Kiaton before turning inland through the mountains to Hercules country. The first of the 'Twelve Labours' had been the slaying of the Nemean lion, which he was supposed to have accomplished with nothing but his bare hands. Some of the strangely eroded rocks did seem to bear a lion's likeness, although Lynn wondered how much of that was due to suggestion rather than actual shape. Peter told her that wine from the local vineyards was even called 'Lion's Blood'.

The Stymphalian lake proved to be little more than a vast, reed-bounded swamp, with a few uninspiring ruins, but the surrounding scenery more than made up for it. Tar macadam gave way to loose gravel and then to dusty earth until they were traversing what was little more than a mountain track. Peter seemed to know where he was going so Lynn could only hang on and hope for the best.

Eventually, after a series of spectacular climbs and descents, they rejoined the proper road again, dropping through red-roofed settlements that tumbled down rugged outcrops of rock to reach the site of the original Greek games in time for lunch.

Shaded by olive and pine, the whole site was

carpeted with wild flowers. Wandering among the
tumbled pillars with a guide-plan in her hand, Lynn
traced the outlines of the stadium and the Altis, the
temples of Zeus and Hera; the Theokalon, which had
been the home of the priests. Over-excavated the place
might be, but it still retained its fascination. For more
than a thousand years, competitors had travelled from
all over Greece and Sicily, even from as far away as
North Africa, to take part in the games—during which
all hostilities between participating states had been
suspended. That fact alone had to be worth
remembering.

Messene, it had already been decided, was going to
have to wait for another day because of the distances
involved. It would be better taking a more direct route
through from Corinth down to Tripolis, Peter had
said the previous evening. Even then it would be a
much longer journey than today's. Lynn thought she
might have to forgo the whole idea. There was only so
much she could do in a couple of weeks.

It was late afternoon when they finally began the
return journey, following the coastline up to Patras
and on to the broad main highway back down to
Corinth. Tired but content, when they at last reached
the hotel, Lynn had time to take a shower and change
her shorts and shirt for a strappy little dress in navy
blue. She had caught the sun again today, she realised,
as she outlined her mouth in pink lipstick at the
bathroom mirror. It had also started to streak her hair
at the front. Two weeks of this weather and no one
was going to believe she had spent the greater part of
it travelling.

The Downings were on the point of leaving as she
reached their shared table. Liz was as red as a
beetroot, every exposed inch of skin glowing with
heat.

'I overdid it,' she acknowledged on a rueful note.

'You always do,' commented her husband without sympathy. 'I cover myself up after ten minutes or so the first couple of days, but not you.'

'I don't burn,' put in Janet with a smug intonation that made Lynn herself want to slap her. 'I can spend as long as I like in the sun and just keep on going browner and browner.' She regarded Lynn critically. 'Is your hair meant to be like that?'

Like what? was the question that sprang immediately to mind, but Lynn refrained from asking it. 'Yes,' she said succinctly.

'Let's go and get that coffee,' said Frank. 'Can't think why they don't serve the damned stuff in here like a civilised restaurant!'

Stavros appeared bearing a fresh platter of salad as the others departed. 'Soup?' he enquired.

'Please.' She gave him a smile, glad to see him back, and added in Greek, 'Did you enjoy your day off?'

From the look on his face she might have been speaking in Urdu, but the surprise only lasted a moment.

'Very much,' he responded. 'I slept all day. You speak our language very well.'

She laughed. 'You're being kind, but thanks for the encouragement. I can use the practice.'

'*Kyrios* Stephanos is fluent in English,' he remarked on a seemingly casual note. 'You will be coming to the discotheque again tonight?'

'I don't think so.' She was careful to keep her own tone as casual. 'I've had a long day.'

Like any other institution, the Amalia obviously possessed a grapevine, she thought amusedly as the waiter departed to fetch her soup. Stavros had not been present last night, she was fairly certain, yet he appeared to be in possession of all the details. Andreas Stephanos was the big boss; she supposed it stood to reason that every move he made would be food for speculation. Thinking about him, she felt the amusement fade. He wasn't going to take kindly to being stood up, yet there had been no definite arrangement to meet, either. She would plead forgetfulness if the question was raised. That might deflate his ego a little.

Noel was waiting for her in the lobby when she left the restaurant. He was out of uniform and wearing slim-fitting slacks and casual shirt in a rust colour that suited his colouring and lean build. There was no sign of Andreas, thank heaven.

'I have a taxi standing by,' he told her. 'How did it go today?'

'Fine,' she said. 'I didn't make Messene though.'

'It was a bit ambitious,' he agreed. 'Did you think about hiring a car to drive yourself? They come expensive, but it would still work out cheaper than a taxi every day.'

'It takes too much concentration. Especially on roads like the ones we met today going across country. I don't want to miss anything.'

'That's a point.' He held the swing door for her, added casually, 'I have the day off on Sunday. If I can swing a one-day hire we could make it via Tripolis.'

The temptation to say yes and have done with it was there, but something held her back. 'It's good of you, but I think I might take the day off Sunday, too.' She laughed. 'I'm beginning to think my whole itinerary might have been over-ambitious!'

'So revise it,' he said. 'Pull in your oars. One day travelling, one day resting, that's the ideal. Might give me a chance to see a bit more of you. I'm not tied up all day and every day.'

'I'll think about it,' she promised.

Almost totally rebuilt after an earthquake in 1928, Corinth itself was a modern sprawl of a town. Lynn had seen it from the toll road earlier and been unimpressed, although its position on the gulf coastline couldn't be bettered. Noel took her to one of the hotel bars, greeting the man behind it with obvious familiarity.

'It's one of a rival company's tour bases,' he confided when they were seated. 'The regular courier is a friend of mine.'

'Male or female?' she asked lightly.

He smiled. 'Female, as a matter-of-fact, but don't read too much into it. I've known Jane for donkey's years!'

'You must meet a lot of girls in this job.'

'Enough. You're the first this season though.'

'There's only been a month of it so far,' she pointed out. 'How many more change-overs does that make?'

He responded to the teasing note in her voice with a grin. 'Enough. You're determined not to take me seriously, aren't you?'

'You wouldn't really want it any other way.'

'No, well, perhaps you're right. Last season I got myself entangled with an Italian girl.' His laugh was wry. 'I had a hard time shaking her off at the end of it!'

'It should have taught you a lesson for the future. Leave the guests alone.'

'Ah, but in you I recognised an independent spirit!' The blue eyes were laughing. 'You wouldn't condemn me to five months of total celibacy, would you?'

That conversation set the tone for the whole evening. Lynn didn't mind. Noel was lightweight, good at his job, and excellent company, but lacking in any form of sensitivity. It was a relationship she could handle. Once or twice she found herself comparing him with Andreas, wondering what the latter was doing. He would know by now that she had left the hotel—and with whom. The duty receptionist had seen them go. Her emotions were confused. Caro meant a lot to her, but involving herself in an affair with the man who had hurt her was hardly going to mend matters. Andreas was no lightweight. What he wanted he would go all out to get. The most sensible course was to steer well clear. Whether that was the course he would allow her to take was another matter.

They were back at the Amalia by eleven-fifteen. Lynn was half relieved, half disappointed to find Andreas conspicious by his absence from the lobby. What might be called over-playing one's hand, she reflected wryly, turning down Noel's invitation to sample the disco on the grounds of being too tired after the day's journeying. A man like Andreas would never be so short of female company that he needed to waste time chasing the apparently reluctant. In all probability he had read her tactics like an open book, and been amused by them. At least it took the onus out of her hands.

Noel went off to the disco alone, leaving her to claim her key from reception. She thought the duty clerk gave her an odd look, but he made no comment other than to wish her a polite 'Kalinihta' in response. There were plenty of people still in the bar and thronging the lounge area. Someone was playing the grand piano—what was commonly called 'tinkling the ivories'—and several were singing along. Already some of the smaller groups had begun to merge, to seek their entertainment *en masse*. Others remained aloof. It took all kinds, Lynn reflected as she climbed the stairs. She was no joiner herself.

Her room was in darkness, the drawn door curtain

shutting out the moonlight. Lynn switched on the two lamps and looked without interest at the wooden-framed bed. She had paid a supplement for a single room, and didn't regret it, yet the doubles were no doubt larger and therefore airier. Sleeping with the balcony doors open meant risking mosquito bites, though at this time of the year there weren't so many around. The sounds from the disco she would just have to put up with until two o'clock.

She was on the balcony when the knock came on the outer door, repeated when she failed to react to it quickly enough. Andreas looked both dark and dangerous in the black slacks and tautly stretched shirt. His only concession to colour lay in the red kerchief knotted at his throat.

'A little late,' he said, 'but the *bouzoukia* stays open till three. Are you ready to go?'

Lynn had kicked off her sandals the moment she got in. Standing there in her bare feet she felt ridiculously small and defenceless. 'I forgot all about it,' she said. 'You'll have to forgive me. Perhaps another night?'

He moved forward into the room, forcing her to step back in order to avoid having her toes trodden on. The strappy high heels were lying where she had dropped them at the end of the bed. Andreas picked them up and held them out to her.

'I've no objection to you looking like a gypsy,' he said, 'but you might find it hard on the soles if you're not used to going barefoot.'

Lynn made no move to take them from him. 'You can't expect me to come out with you at this hour,' she protested. 'I'm tired.'

'I do expect it,' he said, ignoring the plea. 'We had an arrangement. A bad memory is no excuse.'

'Is persistence a Greek trait,' she flashed, 'or a Canadian one?'

His smiled mocked her show of temper. 'It isn't a habit of mine to take no for an answer when I'm well aware it isn't meant.'

'You're so sure of yourself!'

'I'm sure of one thing,' he returned equably, and dropped the sandals to reach out for her, pulling her up to him with hands impossible to defy.

Lynn struggled for a moment before abruptly desisting. Resistance was inflammatory. His mouth was too knowledgeable, lips playing with hers until they parted of their own accord to allow him access. She felt his hands slide the length of her back to cup her hips and bring her up close against him, wanting that contact with an abandonment that was both sudden and flagrant.

Not for Caro, came the fleeting thought. This was for herself. She was going overboard without a life-jacket.

'If we stay here,' he murmured against her lips, 'I'm going to take you to bed with me. Is it what you want?'

It was what she wanted, but not what she dare allow herself. Promiscuity had never been in her line. She detached herself with reluctance from his arms.

'I think you'd better leave,' she said unsteadily.

'Not without you. I alerted the proprietor that I'd be bringing you. Certain factions of his clientele wouldn't appreciate any intrusion by foreigners. Tonight is a good night to go. It may be the only one.' He bent once more to secure her sandals. 'Put them on.'

Lynn did so because there seemed little alternative. He didn't give in easily. Andreas watched without comment as she ran a brush over her hair and applied fresh lipstick. She could see him through the mirror, sitting on the end of her bed as if he had every right in the world to be there. His arrogance should have annoyed her, but it didn't. Not enough. She was going to need to keep on reminding herself of the kind of man he was. Making up to another man's wife was no novelty to him, if last night's performance was anything to go by. Whatever the rights and wrongs of her own conduct, Caro deserved vengeance—if only by proxy.

The duty receptionist gave the two of them what Lynn could only term an 'old-fashioned' look as they crossed the lobby together. In with one man and out again with another less than an hour later was hardly likely to enhance her reputation. The fact that her second choice was none other than the owner himself was likely to add fuel to the speculation.

As she had guessed, the silver Jaguar was indeed Andreas's car. The interior was luxurious.

'I'd have thought you'd import an American car if any,' she said as he started the engine and switched on the powerful headlights.

'I drove the same make in Canada,' he responded equably. 'And I didn't import it. The agents did. Will you fasten your seat-belt? That's another habit I brought back with me. It's compulsory over there.'

Lynn complied without argument. 'In fifteen years you had time to acquire a good few,' she remarked casually. 'Habits, I mean. Did you find it hard to adjust when you first came back?'

'A little,' he admitted. 'But it's surprising how fast it happens. I may sound Canadian, but I never stopped being Greek. Not essentially. There's no place quite like home.'

Lynn said softly, 'If you felt that way I'm surprised you didn't come back earlier. It wasn't as if you couldn't have learned all you needed to know about hotel management right here.'

'My father and I were estranged,' he replied without altering his tone. 'I resented being sent thousands of miles away while my brother stayed here. And to forestall the next question, Dion was killed in a car crash early last year. That's the only reason I'm where I am now. There was no one else to take over.'

Condolences were meaningless when there was no personal knowledge involved, Lynn reflected. She had a feeling that Andreas would neither expect nor appreciate the sentiment if it were expressed. She said instead, 'What about your mother?'

His smile was devoid of the cynicism she had come to associate with him. 'Still very much alive. She lives in Athens.'

'At the hotel you own there?'

'No, privately. A modern flat, to her professed everlasting shame. Secretly she's delighted with all the labour-saving devices. The old family house had few.'

Lynn said in surprise, 'She didn't have help?'

'Only one woman who came in to do the rough work, and only because my father insisted. She hated to be idle. These days she finds interests outside the home.'

They were driving along a darkened minor road with only the occasional sign of habitation in the shape of a small cottage or shed. The moon shed a ghostly light, silvering the landscape.

'Where is this *bouzoukia*?' she asked, abandoning her probe into his past history. 'I thought it was close.'

'It is. Just off the Corinth waterfront, to be exact.'

She said with deliberation, 'I've already been to Corinth once tonight.'

'With your courier,' he agreed. 'Yes, I know.'

She glanced at him swiftly. 'How?'

'I make it my business to be kept advised of certain events.'

'And my movements are among them?'

'Very much so. I knew bare moments after you left the hotel, and the same when you returned.'

'Supposing we hadn't got back until the early hours?' she suggested on a careless note. 'What then?'

'I was giving you until midnight before I came looking for you,' he returned imperturbably. 'As I said before, an arrangement is an arrangement. No woman runs out on me.'

No, she thought with sudden bitterness, only the other way round! Well, it wasn't going to happen to her. Not in any sense. It was time he realised that not everything was his for the taking.

They crossed the main highway a few moments later, heading down through the city to take to a jumble of back streets on the gulf side. Lynn heard the music before they came on its origins, lusty in volume yet almost plaintive in tone. A man was singing, his voice rising and falling in the same discordant pattern, filling the night with hypnotic rhythm.

The club itself was in the cellars of what appeared to be a small and shabby hotel. Looking up at the darkened windows, Lynn wondered how anyone could possibly sleep through the cacophony issuing from directly below. Perhaps, she thought whimsically, it was a house rule that all guests attended the *bouzoukia* until closing time in order to allay complaints. As yet she wasn't at all sure the experience was going to be one she herself might appreciate.

Like nightclubs the world over, the atmosphere was thick and heavy, the lighting dim. The stage, or performing area, was on a level with the surrounding floor, the tables crowded right up to its very edges. Andreas was greeted volubly by a short, stocky man with eyes so sparklingly alive they were a stimulant in themselves. Within moments the two of them were seated at one of the tables fringing the stage, next to a large party of men who all appeared to be having a wonderful time.

The male singer had been replaced by a girl dressed in a slinky garment made from a material that looked like snakeskin, with scales that glistened as she moved. Her looks were striking, her hair a sleek black frame. She had a powerful, rich voice, and was a favourite with the crowd if the carnation heads and smashed plates strewn across the floor were any indication.

A man bearing small round baskets of the flowers threaded his way between the tables. Andreas beckoned him over and secured one of the baskets, pushing it across to Lynn with a smile at her bemused expression.

'What do I do with them?' she shouted, leaning towards him to make herself heard above the hubbub of which the singer was only a part.

'Anything that takes your fancy,' he shouted back. 'If you approve of something, show it!'

As if on cue, a pale pink flower head landed on the table close by Lynn's hand. The three youths on a neighbouring table grinned and waved when she looked across at them. Andreas smiled at her disconcertion.

'Don't try throwing one back,' he warned.

It was impossible to remain unaffected by the sheer atmosphere of the place. Between performers, a man with a broom swept the broken shards of rough-cast pottery to the rear of the stage under the raised dais that held the musicians. Anyone who felt like it just got up and danced regardless of who was on stage at the time, ignored by the artist. Mostly men, Lynn noted. The one female group to take to the floor abandoned their claim to equality after only a few moments, although no verbal discouragement was offered.

She was too fascinated to want to leave, and felt real regret when Andreas finally indicated they should go. Only when they were outside in the comparative quiet did she realise it was almost two o'clock.

'You surprise me,' Andreas commented, putting her into the car. 'I was sure you'd find it too much.'

'I surprised myself,' she confessed. 'At first I thought I would, too. Only it grows on you, that sort of thing. Pulls you in. There were even moments when I wanted to get up and join in—except that women obviously aren't too welcome.'

'It's a man's world,' he agreed, unmoved by the implied criticism. 'The one place where he can go and let off steam in his own fashion. If you'd like to try authentic Greek dancing yourself, I'll take you to a village fiesta.'

'Tonight?' Lynn asked, tongue in cheek, and heard his laugh.

'There's barely enough of it left.' He set the car into motion, glancing at her in the sudden darkness as they left the bright lights and still blaring music behind. 'What did you have planned for tomorrow?'

'Epidauros.' She had her head back against the rest, her eyes closed. 'I had thought of going by local bus.'

'I said I'd take you where you wanted to go.'

'But not when. At least, not definitely.'

'Then I'm telling you now. Tomorrow is yours.'

Her eyes came open. 'All of it?'

'Day and night.' The taunt was back in his voice. 'It isn't an offer I make to everyone.'

It was an offer, Lynn reflected, that she might do well to reject. She opened her mouth, heard her own voice answering. 'The day, then. Do you mind an early start after such a late night?'

'Not if you don't. Shall we say seven-thirty?'

'Breakfast doesn't start until then.'

'So I'll order for the two of us in my suite.'

She forced herself to say it with the right inflection. 'And have whoever brings it up think I spent the night with you? Let's make it eight o'clock instead, then . . .' Her voice lifted in a sudden cry of alarm as two eyes glowed transfixed right in the path of their headlights. 'Look out!'

Andreas hit the brake in a purely reflex action, bringing the car to a skidding halt in the kerb edge. For a long moment there was silence except for the hard release of his breath. When he did speak the tolerance was conspicuous by its absence.

'It was only a cat!'

'I know it was only a cat.' Lynn had been on the verge of apologising for startling him that way; now she gritted her teeth against the urge. 'I happen to be fond of cats.'

'As I happen to be fond of living!'

'I hardly think our lives were endangered,' she retorted with irony. 'If there's any damage to the car I'll pay for it.'

He turned his head to look at her, one brow lifting sardonically. 'In cash or in kind?'

She drew in a breath. 'That was uncalled for!'

He eyed her angry face, his own expression undergoing a subtle alteration. 'I refuse to argue with you over a cat,' he stated. 'We hold different opinions on their value.'

'We hold different opinions on most things!'

'Not true.' The smile was slow. 'Some ways we're in complete accord.'

Lynn stiffened as he took hold of her, but not for long. He unfastened her seat-belt in order to draw her closer, cherishing her mouth with sensually charged kisses until she responded in kind.

'Put your hands on me,' he murmured against her

lips. 'I want to feel your touch. Under my shirt, not over it.'

Lynn obeyed as if in a dream, unfastening the buttons of the black shirt to slide both hands over bare skin, feeling the run of muscle beneath her fingers, the crisp curl of hair; her senses responding instinctively to the warm, musky scent of his body.

His flesh tasted faintly salty, tingling her tongue. She felt totally uninhibited; conscious of the need to touch, to arouse this man the way he was arousing her. He had drawn the thin straps of her dress down over her shoulders, baring both breasts to his sensual exploration. Her nipples were hardened, thrusting proud of the surrounding flesh—begging the lips he bent towards them. She arched her back in an ecstasy of sensation as he ran the very tip of his tongue over one tender, aching peak, fastening her fingers in the black hair to bring his head closer and hold him captive.

Caro had been here like this before her, came the sudden thought like a dash of cold water down her back. Her own sister! She sat back abruptly, tugging at her straps with fingers gone suddenly clumsy.

'It's late,' she said. 'We should get back.'

'A moment ago that was the last thought in your mind.' His voice held a curious note. 'You were ready, even eager to take things further. Why the change?'

'Isn't it allowed?' Lynn was defensive, aware he spoke the truth. She had been ready to do just about anything he asked, and for purely physical reasons. Knowing it didn't make her proud. 'I got carried away, but not far enough. You'll have to accept it.'

'I don't *have* to do anything,' he returned with a harder inflection. 'Don't play games with me, Lynn!'

She made herself look at him, closing her mind to the macho appeal of his bared chest and smouldering eyes. He had played games with Caro; why should he be the only one?

'I don't want you to think I'm easy,' she got out, choosing her words with care. 'I don't come on that way for every man I meet.'

He was silent for a moment studying her, his expression enigmatic. 'I'm flattered,' he said at length. 'And sorry if I overstepped the limit. From now on I'll take more care.'

She had lost yet another opportunity to escape from this association, and it wasn't going to get any easier. Despise his kind she might, but there was no denying his power to attract. Lynn had a suspicion she might live to regret her involvement.

CHAPTER FOUR

EPIDAURUS was everything Lynn had anticipated, and a little more. Set amidst pine glades and backed by the flower-clad lower slopes of Mount Kynortion, the almost perfectly preserved amphitheatre was awe-inspiring in its sheer spectacle. To stand on the topmost level of the fifty-five curving tiers and look down the gangway just climbed was to create instant vertigo, she discovered, groping for a seat before attempting to focus her camera.

'You can buy excellent views from the site shops,' Andreas remarked, watching her fiddle with light settings and distances. 'Failing that, there are cameras that do all the work for you.'

'It doesn't provide the same satisfaction,' Lynn responded mildly. 'Though I might buy a postcard as a fallback just in case.'

'No faith in your technique?' he jeered.

She clicked the shutter before answering, refusing to rise to the taunt. 'I'm not infallible.' Eyes on the scene still spread before them, she added regretfully, 'It never comes across in any real sense anyway. You have to *feel* the atmosphere in a place like this. If I closed my eyes I could almost imagine myself back in the fourth century B.C.!'

'If you close your eyes you'll probably go dizzy again,' warned Andreas on a practical note. 'I think it's time we went down and found ourselves some lunch. Did you see everything you wanted to see?'

'I think so.'

'In that case, we'll go and look for a *taverna*. It's going to be far too crowded here with all the coach parties.'

He descended ahead of her, the breadth of his back providing a bulkhead against which to fall. A group of three well-built girls wearing the briefest of shorts and sun tops were ascending the same gangway. They stepped sideways into one of the tiers to allow the two of them free passage, the foremost of the group eying Andreas in bold appraisal.

'*Schon weiter, fahren,*' she said.

Andreas expressed his thanks in the same language, adding something unintelligible to Lynn's ears that drew an appreciative laugh from the recipient.

'I didn't realise you spoke German, too,' she commented when they were back on level ground again. 'What was it she said?'

'Just "pass, friend"' he translated easily. 'We came in from the left, didn't we?'

Lynn murmured an agreement. She would have given a great deal to know exactly what it was *he* had said in return, but he obviously wasn't going to tell her. In his white slacks and dark blue shirt, with his hair ruffled by the breeze, he was more compellingly attractive than any man had a right to be. He knew it, too—and played on it. Even though he was with her he hadn't been able to resist the sexy little exchange with the girl back there. She may not be able to speak the language, but she could recognise a certain familiar response in another's eyes.

'You're looking pensive,' he said as they moved down the tree-lined path towards the main entrance. 'Something bothering you?'

Jealousy was the word that best described her present emotion, she reflected wryly, but it was the last thing she was going to acknowledge. It was the last thing she wanted to feel, if it came to that.

'I'm hungry,' she said, and forced a laugh. 'I'm

surprised you can't hear my stomach complaining!'

Coaches and cars were still rolling into the parking area. Andreas had a difficult task extracting the Jaguar from the jam of vehicles left without regard to marked lines. The mountains were hazy in the midday heat, the sky overhead so bright it hurt the eyes to look up.

There was air-conditioning in the car, but Andreas drove with all windows fully opened instead, creating havoc with Lynn's hair until she slipped on the bandeau she had worn earlier. The red shorts she was wearing pulled taut across the top of her thighs when she sat, too form-fitting for either comfort or modesty. She felt Andreas's glance and wondered what he was thinking. In all probability he was taking it as a deliberate come-on on her part, when if the truth were known she simply hadn't realised just how tight the darned things were.

He found his taverna with unerring instinct right off the beaten track, a shabby old building two storeys high, with walls that had once been whitewashed but were now faded to an overall grey. A low, glass-fronted extension had been added, from which stretched a canvas awning covering the dusty eating area scattered with wooden tables and chairs. Three goats and a donkey grazed the sparse grass a few yards away, picking their way between the rusting relics of at least two dismembered vehicles.

Despite the somewhat isolated locality, there were other cars already parked out front, and people seated with food in front of them. Delicious smells issued forth from the interior.

Andreas chose a table close by the edge of the canvas where they could be under shade but still catch the cooling breeze. A youth wearing the inevitable uniform of white shirt and dark trousers appeared from within bearing a square of plastic which he used to cover the table surface, ripping each corner at the centre and tying the two ends securely about the legs.

They went inside to the primitive kitchen to choose their own fish from a battered refrigerator. The solitary old woman doing the cooking seemed unaffected by the heat and smoke, although Lynn found both overwhelming. She was glad to get outside again in the fresh air.

More diners had arrived, every table was now occupied. Obviously the place had a reputation for good food. No one seemed in any hurry. Voices rose and fell in amicable conversation.

'I love this time of day,' Lynn acknowledged, tackling both salad and crusty bread with gusto when it arrived. 'Everything tastes so much better when it's eaten *al fresco*.'

'You should live here,' said Andreas idly. 'The climate suits you. Or better still, further south—say Crete. Down there the weather stays pleasant most of the year round.'

'You have a hotel there, too, don't you?' she asked. 'Though I suppose Athens is your base.'

'I don't have a base. Not yet. I haven't decided what the future is going to be.'

'I'd have thought it was cut and dried. You said you were the only one of the family able to take over where your father left off.'

'True, but that doesn't necessarily mean I have to continue along the exact same path.'

Lynn considered that in silence for a moment or two. 'Do you mean you might consider selling out?' she asked at length.

'It's a possibility. Apart from the Hellas and the Amalia, that is. They're close enough to keep an eye on without spending all my time travelling.'

'You don't trust your management?'

'Depends what you mean by trust. Our priorities are different. We have to move with the times if we want to attract more of the tourist trade. These who come to Greece on their own initiative are generally satisfied with whatever they can find in the way of accommodation, and wouldn't want it any other way, but the package tourist looks for all the home comforts and conveniences, and expects them to work when they're available. There's time and money wasted all the way down the line, and no excuse for it.'

She was watching his mouth as he spoke, stomach muscles tautening to the faint curl of his upper lip. The Greek side of his nature was not much in evidence at the moment. His tone held such cutting authority, his eyes a light of intolerance. Ruthless, she thought. Caring about nothing or no one except his own ideals. It was perhaps too sweeping an assessment, but she was suddenly in no mood to be fair.

'You can hardly expect to apply Canadian standards over here,' she protested. 'They're two different worlds.'

'Outside,' he agreed. 'I'm no more in favour of the concrete blocks springing up all over the place than anyone else. Efficiency doesn't have to be soulless. Tourism is an essential factor in the country's economy. If we want them to keep coming we have to provide the basics.'

'The basics you already have,' Lynn pointed out. 'You're talking about luxuries.'

He studied her for a moment before answering, eyes narrowed a little. 'You're deliberately picking an argument. Why the aggravation?'

'I suppose I'm just reluctant to see Greece become another Spain, that's all.'

'I doubt if it could. Our coastline isn't cut out for it.'

The arrival of their fish put a temporary end to discussion. Forking the first sizzling portion of pink-tinted flesh into her mouth, Lynn thought she hadn't tasted anything quite as good since the previous year in Thessaly. The mere mention of Canada had unsettled her. The question when it came was over-casual.

'Did you make a lot of friends in Toronto? Personal ones, I mean?'

'Women, you mean.' He shrugged easily. 'I'm thirty-three years old, and normally adjusted. What do you think?'

'I think,' she said with deliberation, 'that you probably belong to the love 'em and leave 'em brigade. You were never married, were you?'

'Not even once.' His tone mocked. 'If there's one thing most women can't bear it's a man who managed to escape the matrimonial bed!'

Lynn smiled at him blandly. 'One of these days you might find yourself hoist by your own petard.'

'If that means what I think it means, how do you know it hasn't already happened?'

'Because nothing touches you,' she said. 'You do exactly as you want when you want and go merrily on your way.'

'You've known me exactly three days,' he pointed out. 'That hardly gives you the authority to make statements like that one.'

'So sue me for defamation of character.'

His smile flicked her lazily. 'I can think of other things I'd like to do with you right this moment, if the venue were more conducive.'

The same things he had done with her sister, no doubt, she thought drily. She had to keep reminding herself of that fact. She couldn't afford to forget it.

It was almost three by the time they finished off the

meal with cups of the syrupy sweet Turkish coffee. Andreas was the first to glance at his watch.

'If we're going to Mycenae we should be on our way,' he said. 'I have an engagement this evening.'

'We could go straight back now,' Lynn offered, stifling the swift little pang. 'I could fit Mycenae in with Old Corinth on Monday.'

The shake of the dark head was decisive. 'You'll need the whole day if you want to climb to the old fortresses at Acrocorinth. The view alone is worth the effort.'

From the sound of it that was one trip he wasn't planning on making with her. Hardly surprising really, Lynn reflected. Trailing round in someone's wake all day was apt to curb the most generous spirit. It was possible he had decided to give her up as a bad job rather than continue to pursue a relationship with so little promise. Last night she had made it all too clear that she wasn't on the market for a casual affair. In some ways it would be almost a relief if he left her alone. She wasn't up to the task she had set herself.

She purposely avoided all contact during the rest of the afternoon, whether to test him or herself she wasn't at all sure. If he noticed he gave no indication of it, standing patiently by while she lined up shots of the Lion Gate. There were too many people around to make the latter worthwhile. She finished up buying one of the professionally photographed postcards in the end, as she had done at Epidaurus. It would be necessary to be here either very early in the morning or right out of season to find the place devoid of tourists, she supposed wryly. She was one herself, if it came to that.

They were back at the Amalia for six-thirty, to find the lobby thronged with people both coming and going. Andreas accepted her thanks for the day they had spent, his expression faintly quizzical.

'I'm glad you enjoyed it,' he said. 'Tomorrow, I'm already committed, though . . .'

Whatever he had been about to say was lost as the duty receptionist called his name. The man was standing in the office doorway looking harassed, one hand held up close by his ear in a sign that was universal. Andreas excused himself and went to take the call, leaving Lynn to make her way upstairs with mixed feelings. Her suspicions, it seemed, had been correct. Andreas obviously considered he had wasted enough time. It had been a lousy idea anyway, she comforted herself. She was well out of it.

She finished dinner around nine after listening to a running account of the Downings' day. Janet had become friendly with the son of another English couple from the Midlands, and was full of plans for an evening at the disco. Frank's attempt to lay down the law with regard to time of retirement was met with derision from both mother and daughter, quelling him into resigned silence. Lynn felt almost sorry for him. He was both outnumbered and outclassed when it came to verbal battles.

The heat of the day had capitulated to velvety warmth. Avoiding the crowded terrace, Lynn wandered through the grounds, coming eventually on a gate leading out on to the unpaved road which wound through the scattered villas. Lights twinkled invitingly, outlining patios and pools. Music and laughter came clearly across on the still air. Weekend homes for city dwellers for the most part, Noel had told her, although one or two were occupied all year round.

Strolling along, listening to the sounds of revelry, she felt a pang of nostalgia for family weekends she could remember when the four of them had barbecued steaks and beefburgers out on their own little patio and eaten them under the stars. A lot had happened since then, not all of it good. Caro's departure for Canada had been hard enough for their parents to take, but her pending divorce was worse.

She came to the end of the road where the land fell gently away towards the sea, standing for a moment to look at a villa set further down the slope. There must be another road, she realised. Certainly there was no approach from this direction.

Little privacy either, because she was looking directly into one of the lighted, unshuttered windows at the man and woman so intimately conversing just beyond the glass. Andreas was smiling that lazy, smile of his, his lips moving on words his companion clearly found pleasant to hear. Her hands rested lightly on his shoulders, his on her waist. They had either just stopped kissing or were about to start; which, Lynn was in no mood to find out. She turned jerkily away to retrace her steps, stumbling over the uneven surface as her heel slipped.

So she hadn't been mistaken the other night; there was something between those two. The question of where the woman's husband and son were was hardly relevant. If they were around, that little scene back there wouldn't be taking place. Men like Andreas only played their games when the coast was clear. Already committed, the latter had said. She knew now to what. Caro and this Greek woman, and how many more? How many broken marriages lay in his trail? Caro was at least childless. This other woman had a son she should be thinking of. Except that people like her didn't think about anything or anyone else but themselves, did they? A reflection which included her sister, too, when it came right down to it.

She was almost back at the hotel before she had her emotions under control. Be rational, she told herself.

You knew what he was. You'd already decided there was no point in fighting a lost cause, so why let it bother you?

She knew why, of course. Despite everything, she had let him get to her. Only he didn't know that, and he wasn't going to know. From now on she would put him out of her mind.

Noel 'phoned her room before breakfast next morning to ask if she fancied spending the day with some friends of his who were staying down the coast at Portochellon. He had managed to borrow a car so there was no transport problem. The friends, he added, were spending a few weeks in the area aboard the boat they had sailed here from England. They had promised to take a trip across to Spetsae. Lynn didn't need asking twice. She had nothing planned until tomorrow anyway.

It turned out to be one of the most enjoyable days she had spent in ages. Tim and Sue were a couple in their late twenties who spent their winters working their asses off, to put it in their own vernacular, and the summers from May to September cruising the warmer waters around the Mediterranean.

'There was a time when we thought about getting married and settling down with a couple of kids,' Sue confessed cheerfully to Lynn at one point when the two of them were alone below decks preparing a snack in the yacht's tiny galley. 'Then we thought what the hell! You only live once. Everything we earn goes into this old tub. She's in her dotage, but still seaworthy. Maybe when she finally gives it up we'll do the same—if we're still together by then. She's good for another ten years with care.' She slanted a glance, curiosity unconcealed. 'You and Noel? Are you . . .'

'Just a holiday friendship,' Lynn replied without undue emphasis. 'I'm only here for a couple of weeks.'

'You don't seem the type to take a package holiday,' came the frank comment. 'With your looks you could be living it up on the Riviera!'

Lynn laughed. 'With some sugar daddy for company?'

'The rich age fast. It's a fact of life,' Sue was laughing too. 'Something Tim and I don't need worry about, that's for sure!'

Spetsae proved to be one of the prettiest of the inshore Greek islands with its pine-covered hills and dazzling pink-and-white buildings. The four of them spent a long and lazy afternoon exploring the narrow streets and colourful shops. Lynn bought one of the embroidered blouses for about a third less than the hotel prices, glad she had waited. Later they moored off one of the tiny rocky coves on the island's south side and swam in the translucent waters before returning to the mainland to watch the sunset over an evening meal at one of the waterfront tavernas.

It was fully dark by the time they broke up the party. Lynn sat back into her seat in the car with a small sigh of regret as they pulled away.

'That's been a good day,' she said. 'I'm sorry it's over.'

'So am I,' Noel agreed. 'Pity they're not going to be here next Sunday. It's an idyllic way to spend a summer don't you think?'

'One perhaps. I'm not sure I could do it every year.'

'Oh, they always manage to find places they haven't visited before.'

It wasn't what she had meant but she let it pass. With the distractions of the day now absent, she found herself wondering how Andreas had spent his time, lingering with masochistic insistence on the mental picture of him and that woman last night. She had no cause to feel betrayed, yet she did. The taste of it was in her mouth, bitter as aloes. Her own fault, of course, for being so foolish as to imagine she could entangle herself with a man of his type and escape unscathed. He had made an art of persuading women to fall for him.

'You're very quiet,' Noel commented after a while. 'Tired?'

'Pleasantly.' Lynn made a conscious effort to stir herself into a more responsive frame of mind. 'I was thinking about tomorrow and what I need to fit in.'

'If I wasn't tied up with the Olympia trip I'd come with you,' he said regretfully. 'What about Tuesday?'

She was cautious. 'I'm not sure. You're on the islands tour, aren't you?'

'Only as far as the docks. I spend the morning in Athens with the Area rep turning in my weekly report, etcetera.' His tone lightened. 'Hey, that's an idea. Why not come on in with us on the coach? There's always a spare seat. You could do the Acropolis before it gets too hot or too crowded, then meet me for lunch.'

'You're right,' she said, 'it is an idea.' Still she hesitated. 'Can I let you know?'

'Sure.' If he was disappointed by her lack of alacrity in accepting the offer he wasn't making any song and dance about it. 'Anytime you're ready.'

They arrived back at the Amalia to find a party in full swing celebrating the silver wedding anniversary of a couple in the British contingent. Noel was seized upon on sight, Lynn along with him. Plied with Metaxa, they surrendered themselves to the inevitable and joined in the fun.

One man with a guitar and an excellent baritone voice sang country-and-western for the entertainment of all, including a party of Italians seated out on the terrace. Someone else did impressions. Laughing at one of the latter, Lynn found her eyes drawn to the lobby steps, to see Andreas leaning negligently against one of the supporting pillars as he watched the proceedings. Catching her eye, he lifted a hand in greeting, turning the gesture into a beckoning motion accompanied by that lazy smile of his. Lynn turned her back on him ostentatiously. When she did finally steal another glance some minutes later he had gone, a fact which left her feeling wholly deflated.

The gathering finally broke up at midnight when somebody suggested retiring to the disco for the last couple of hours.

'It's going to be bedlam down there when that lot arrive,' Lynn commented to Noel in the lobby as the sounds of revelry faded into the middle distance. 'I don't think I could face another two hours.' She smiled at him. 'It's been a super day, Noel. Thanks for asking me.'

'Thanks for coming.' He nodded towards the stairs. 'I'll walk up with you.'

There were exactly twenty-three of the wide stone treads to the first floor. Reaching the landing, Lynn gave the courier another smile. 'Good night.'

He took hold of her suddenly and kissed her, blue eyes lit by the light of determination. 'You're not too good for the old ego,' he said. 'But there's time yet. 'Night, Lynn. Don't forget about Tuesday.'

Turning along her own corridor, Lynn tried to convince herself that she had no cause to feel guilty about taking advantage of the offer, and knew it wasn't going to work. Noel might only want a light-hearted affair for the duration of her fortnight but it was more than she was willing to give. If he wouldn't settle for being simply friends then she had to stop encouraging him, and that meant no more trips.

The curtains were already drawn in her room,

revealing by their slight movement that the sliding doors behind them were at least partially opened. Lynn went to close them, stifling an involuntary scream as the man lounging in one of the low-slung plastic chairs outside on the balcony swung his head towards her.

'Come and join me,' Andreas invited sociably. 'Or shall I come inside?'

'How did you get in here?' she demanded. 'What right have you . . .?'

The calm explanation cut across her protests. 'I borrowed the spare key. It was the only way I could be sure of pinning you down. Where were you all day?'

'Out.' She used the word with force. 'And that's where I'd like you to be. Right now, if you don't mind!'

'The English have a confusing way of issuing orders.' His tone mocked her anger. 'Of course I mind. I came to talk.'

'Oh *sure* you did! I've had experience of your brand of conversation before, remember!' She was trembling, not quite in control of her emotions. 'Just leave me alone, Andreas. I'm not here to provide you with light relief!'

'I want to apologise for leaving you so abruptly last night,' he continued as though she hadn't spoken. 'I looked for you later.'

Lynn stayed where she was, one hand clutching the door frame. He had neither looked very hard nor waited very long. But then he had had other matters on his mind. 'You don't owe me any explanations,' she said tautly. 'I'm grateful for the time you spent taking me to Epidaurus, of course, but there was never any obligation. As a matter of fact, I'm better on my own.'

Dark brows lifted a fraction. 'Then there isn't much point in my offering to take you to Old Corinth tomorrow?'

Her heart leapt then steadied again 'None at all,' she said flatly. 'I don't need the distraction.'

'It's some small comfort to know I'm at least that.' He pressed himself to his feet, lips twisting as she took a step backwards into the room. 'Short of leaping from the balcony, there's only one way I can leave and that's the way I came, which means passing you at some point. I'm not going to ask what caused this sudden change in disposition. It isn't all that important. Just be confident. I shan't jump on you.'

'Good,' was all she could think of to say. She moved to the dressing-table to let him pass, stifling the urge to reach out and touch the bare, bronzed arm. The attraction he had for her was merely physical. She would get over it.

Andreas paused at the door, fingers resting on the handle as he glanced back to where she stood. 'A word of warning,' he said, 'if you're planning to climb to Acrocorinth on your own. It's lonely up there this time of year, and the fortress ruins can be dangerous. There are several deep wells, not all of them securely covered. Fall in one and you'll never get out.'

'I'll keep my eyes open.' Her tone was short. 'Good night.'

Only after the door had closed behind him did she allow herself to relax. That was that. He wouldn't bother with her again. So much for all her grandiose plans. She sent a wry mental apology winging her sister's way.

CHAPTER FIVE

THE bus was crowded, not only with people, but also with wicker baskets holding various produce, with parcels and boxes, with packets of mail to be dropped off along the way on the round journey from Corinth back to Corinth. Squashed in between a black-attired granny carrying a live hen in her lap and two small but lively children, Lynn was half deafened by the cheerful cacophony of voices exchanging news and gossip above the blare of the driver's radio playing the latest record releases. She was the only non-Greek on the vehicle.

No journey by local transport was ever direct. Corinth lay only a few miles from Isthmia but every village, no matter how tiny, had to be visited first. At almost every crossroads there were people waiting, sometimes to board, sometimes to pick up incoming goods and mail, often just to exchange a few words with those travelling abroad. By the time they finally trundled into the town itself it was almost eight o'clock and already getting hot.

Having missed breakfast due to her early start, she took a few minutes to eat a roll and drink a cup of coffee at a café near the bus station, before attempting the next stage of her journey to the site of the ancient city which lay a few kilometres further on. Resolutely she closed her mind to the thought of how much easier the whole excursion would have been in Andreas' company. If a thing was worth doing at all it was surely worth a little trouble. This way she only had herself to please.

She arrived at her ultimate destination around nine, to find the tree-shaded main street already thronged with traffic of all descriptions. The archaeological site lay just beyond the village, its tumbled remains dominated by the seven columns which were all that was left of the original Temple of Apollo. A riot of yellow mimosa captured the sunlight. Far above, topping the rugged heights of the mountain, could be seen crenellated walls and the ruins of yet another temple.

Later, Lynn decided, bringing her attention back to lower levels again. The whole day lay ahead. She sniffed pleasurably at the lemon-scented air, refusing to admit to a certain lack of enthusiasm for her planned itinerary. She was here to work; that had been her intention from the start. From now on she concentrated solely on that aspect.

The morning passed quickly enough. After viewing the museum she tagged on behind a party of French, admiring the guide's technique in mingling fact with fable. Capturing interest was one thing, retaining it for the duration quite another. It was an idea worth adopting herself.

Aware from her guide book that there was a *taverna* close by the fortress gates, she made an arrangement with a taxi driver to take her up the winding mountain road and return for her in three hours, hoping she could trust the man to keep his word. It was delightful sitting out under the awning drinking iced lemonade and nibbling crisply fried whitebait. Far below, a panorama of cultivated fields and citrus groves stretched to the distant gulf, the air between shimmering in the heat. Apart from a couple of youths who had arrived on a motorcycle shortly after her, and the man who had served her, the place seemed deserted. Some few hundred yards above at the head of a steep, stony path, lay the first of the arched gateways, flanked by crumbling stone walls which meandered across the hillside. There was still a long way to go to reach the main site of the fortress, but she felt bound to make the effort having come this far.

The youths made kissing noises with their mouths as she passed their table. Lynn ignored them. She had pulled on a thin cotton shirt over her suntop, tying the front corners at her waist. With a small red scarf knotted about her head and lotion rubbed over her exposed skin she felt reasonably protected against the sun's rays.

For fifteen minutes or so she made good headway, then the heat began to get to her, slowing her steps and shortening her breath. The path was rough, mounting the hillside in a series of curves which doubled the length of the journey. A second great gateway provided shade for a rest and another look at the superb view, then it was on again until she eventually turned the shoulder of the hill to follow the overgrown remains of the inner wall.

From this side the view was of mountains, range after range fading into haze. Flowers splashed the tall grasses with colour. Lynn breathed in the scent of rosemary and wild thyme, avoiding the needle-sharp spines of a lethal-looking plant growing across the path. Except for the humming of bees and the occasional cry of a bird there was no sound. It was like being cut off from the world.

She had been sitting for several minutes on a broken portion of the ramparts, lost in the view, when her eye caught the sign of movement back along the path she had recently traversed. The two youths from the *taverna* were moving in file, eyes fixed on the broken ground ahead. The foremost one looked up and saw her at almost the same moment she saw them, glancing back to make some comment to his companion. Ribald laughter shattered the peace and sent a sudden frisson of foreboding the length of Lynn's spine. If they had followed her up here it wasn't for any healthy reason. Not those two. With their bold eyes and overlong hair, their uniform of dirty jeans and tatty T-shirts, they were anything but reassuring.

She hadn't moved when they reached her, for the simple reason that there was nowhere she could go. The two of them stopped a few feet away, eyeing her slim bare legs with all too apparent lewdness of thought. One said something in a language that sounded like Italian, shrugging his shoulders and grinning when she intimated her lack of comprehension. His glance towards his companion was meaningful.

Back along the track another figure topped the final rise, pausing for a moment to scan the terrain ahead. Instinctively, Lynn shot up a hand and waved, causing the two in front of her to look sharply to their rear. There was a moment when she thought they were going to stand their ground, but as the newcomer began coming forward again they seemed to come to the same reluctant decision, throwing her sullen glances before moving on.

The pent-up breath came out of her in a long-drawn sigh of sheer relief as they disappeared from view beyond a section of wall. How or why Andreas came to be up here at just the right moment didn't matter. It was enough that he was there.

There was a certain grimness about his expression when he reached her.

'What were those two after?' he demanded.

'Your guess is as good as mine,' she said, unsurprised by the tremor in her voice. 'They didn't actually do anything.'

'Only because I happened to arrive when I did.' His gaze moved over her with deliberation. 'Don't you think it might be wiser to wear something a little less provocative when you're on your own this way?'

'Meaning I was asking for it, I suppose?' The relief had flown, replaced by an anger made all the more intense by a suspicion that he might have a valid point. 'How like a man!'

'Oh, I agree a woman should be able to walk around stark naked, if she wants to, without being molested.' His voice was heavy with irony. 'Unfortunately, this doesn't happen to be a perfect world!'

'And the male of the species is easily over-stimulated,' she rejoined, borrowing the same tone. 'You should know!'

He studied her for a long moment without moving, taking in the hectic flush of her cheeks, the fire in her eyes. When he did speak it was with rather less force. 'I'm not here to fight with you, Lynn.'

'No?' She stayed where she was on the rampart, not trusting her legs to hold her without trembling— whether from fury or delayed reaction she wasn't sure. 'If it comes to that, what *are* you doing here?'

'I came looking for you,' he acknowledged. 'On impulse. It seemed reasonable to suppose you'd either be up here already or would be arriving during the course of the afternoon.' He was speaking quietly now, succinctly. 'The waiter told me he'd seen you making for the gate. He also mentioned those two young thugs, so I made all haste.'

'I'm grateful.'

'There's no charge.'

Lynn bit her lip. 'All right, so I should have been more careful. I will be in future.' She eyed him stonily. 'I thought we said everything there was to say last night.'

'Nothing that explained your reasons for turning against me.'

'Do I need a reason?'

'*I* need one,' he said. 'You were angry about something. I want to know what it was I'd said or done to make you feel that way.'

'So you can avoid making the same mistake with your next victim?' Her tone was scathing. 'I was under the impression you preferred married women anyway!'

The dark eyes flickered but his tone remained steady. 'I'm not sure what I'm supposed to infer from that.'

Lynn shrugged, already wishing she had left the whole thing alone. It was too late now. He wasn't going to let her get away with the observation. 'I was out walking Saturday evening,' she said. 'I saw you with your friend's wife.'

'My friend's wife?' he repeated blankly, and then on a sudden note of realisation, 'You mean Alexis and Elina?'

'If that's the couple you were entertaining Thursday night, yes.'

'They're not man and wife,' he said. 'Elina is his sister. His wife left him and their son for another man two years ago.'

The pause was lengthy. Lynn rallied with an effort. 'So I misunderstood. It's none of my business anyway.'

Andreas moved to block her as she got to her feet. The strong features had a determined cast. 'What exactly was it you saw?'

'You were in a clinch close by the villa window,' she said. 'Hardly important now, is it?'

'Important enough if it concerned you at the time.'

'It only concerned me because I thought you were carrying on behind a friend's back.'

His gaze pierced her through. 'Even though you've never even met Alexis?'

'It isn't necessary to know the people concerned to feel indignation on their behalf.'

'His behalf or your own?' he queried. 'It must have appeared as if I'd gone straight from you to her.'

Lynn looked away from him. 'You'd taken me out for the day, that's all. Why should I personally care who you saw afterwards?'

'If it meant nothing to you you wouldn't have mentioned it at all,' he observed, not unreasonably. 'Alexis asked me to have dinner with them on Saturday. It was only afterwards that Elina told me the invitation had been her idea.'

Lynn was drawn despite herself. 'So you made love to her to oblige!'

'I kissed her,' he corrected. 'Unfortunately, some women find it difficult to accept that a man might fail to be totally enamoured.'

'Kissing her is hardly likely to convince her otherwise.'

'Short of being extremely blunt I saw no way out of it.' There was a hint of irony in his voice. 'Perhaps an indulgence on my part. Kissing an attractive woman was never an abhorrent task. Anyway, there you have it.'

He was still blocking her, making it impossible for her to pass without touching him. She felt totally at odds with herself. He might have explained away one liaison satisfactorily but it still left her sister.

Andreas resolved the dilemma by pulling her into his arms, holding her firmly until she stopped struggling and started to respond to his kiss, lips softening, blindly moving. She had taken off her shirt in order to get some sun on her shoulders. The grassy bank felt rough to her bare skin. Some faint protest sprang to her lips when he drew down her knitted tube of a suntop, but the erotic sensation as his mouth enclosed one already hardened nipple was too much for flesh and blood to withstand. The moan was wrenched from somewhere deep down, followed by another as his tongue traced a path from one breast to the other. She had her fingers fastened in the dark thickness of his hair, her eyes closed against the glare of the sun, her every sense tuned to the passage of his hands and mouth over her body. No other man had ever aroused her this far this fast: perhaps, came the thought, because she had never allowed any other man the same leeway.

'No!' she said huskily, feeling his fingers at the zip of her shorts. 'That's far enough!'

There was a moment when she thought he was going to ignore her and carry on, then abruptly he shoved himself up and away, sitting with an arm across one bent knee and his head turned away from her.

'You tempt me to do something I never had cause to contemplate before,' he growled. 'What kind of game are you playing with me?'

'It isn't a game.' She stirred to adjust the suntop, miserably aware that he had some cause to be angry. 'I just don't happen to think this is the right place. Someone might come.'

He turned his head to look at her then, breathing still a little roughened but under control. His expression was hard to decipher. 'You mean if we were somewhere else less exposed you'd be more forthcoming?'

She sat up herself before answering, not meeting his eyes. 'I suppose what I really mean is I'm not on the market for a cheap holiday affair.'

'And you're so sure that's all I'm interested in myself?'

Lynn forced herself to look at him directly. 'Well, isn't it?'

He took a moment to reply. The shrug when it came was philosophical. 'I'd dispute the word cheap, and we're neither of us on holiday as such, but it's true that I want you. I can hardly deny it. If you felt this way why didn't you tell me you wanted nothing more to do with me?'

'I tried to,' she pointed out. 'Last night.'

He shook his head. 'Last night you made nothing clear.'

'Well, you know now.' Lynn got to her feet, striving to appear on top of the situation. 'I'm going down. I have a taxi coming for me at four.'

They made the descent from the fortress together and in near silence, Andreas offering a helping hand over the rough patches where loose stone made the path hazardous. Lynn was relieved to find the motorcycle gone from the front of the *taverna*. She couldn't have faced seeing those sneering faces again.

The Jaguar was parked in the scant shade offered by a solitary tree. Andreas made no attempt to move towards it, indicating the nearest table.

'I think we could both of us do with a long cool drink. Do you like the Greek beer?'

Lynn nodded, sinking into a seat to rub her aching calf muscles. 'I'm out of condition,' she stated ruefully, more for something to say than from any need of sympathy.

'It's a hard climb, and you probably tried to make it too fast.' He gave an order to the waiter who appeared in the doorway behind them, then sat down himself, resting a forearm on the table top. His profile had a chiselled edge. 'My fault,' he announced unexpectedly. 'I allowed my feelings to get out of hand.' The smile he turned on her was quizzical. 'The effect you have on me.'

'It's all right.' She scarcely knew what else to say. 'I didn't mean to provoke you.'

Something sparked momentarily in the darkness of his eyes, and was gone. When he spoke he sounded relaxed enough. 'So we start over.'

The leap of her heart was belied by the steadiness of her voice. 'Wouldn't it be better if we didn't spend any more time together?'

'I don't think so. Providing we both know where we stand. I can save you both time and money this coming week.'

'Your commitments . . .' Lynn began.

He shrugged again. 'There's nothing that can't be put aside—apart from Sunday, that is. My mother has to take priority.'

'That's where you were yesterday?'

'I spend every Sunday with her when I'm in reach of Athens.' He smiled at her expression. 'Not what you'd expect from me?'

'Not really.' She studied him confusedly. A part of her wanted very much to go along with what he was suggesting, but the memory of who and what he was still intruded. Yet she didn't have to be right, did she? If she could accept one unlikely coincidence then why not another? There had to be other Greeks domiciled in Canada, and Andreas was hardly a rare name. The only sure way to find out was to ask him, and she couldn't bring herself to do that.

So forget it, she thought in sudden recklessness. Pretend the question had never even arisen. There was no future in this relationship anyway, so why not enjoy the present? They were going to have little enough time together to waste it in useless speculation.

'I'd like to meet her,' she added on impulse. 'Would it be possible?'

'I don't see why not.' If he was surprised by the

request he wasn't revealing it. 'You'll still be here next weekend.'

Another whole week. And she was going to make the most of it, Lynn told herself firmly. Whatever might have happened in Andreas' past, that was where it belonged.

They packed a lot into those following days, visiting all the major archaeological sites within reach by car, and still finding time to swim and sunbathe and just generally laze around. In the evenings it was dinner in Corinth or nearby Loutraki, and once as far as Athens itself—all of which, Lynn had to admit, she enjoyed a great deal more than the fare she had already paid for. If occasionally she knew a pang of disappointment that Andreas was keeping his word in making no serious emotional demands on her, that was all she allowed herself. Keeping the whole thing on a semi-platonic level was by far the best way. Come the end of her fortnight she would at least be able to take her leave of him with self-respect intact.

Noel viewed the association with a somewhat jaundiced eye, although with his spare time taken over by a cute little redhead from the new intake he was hardly deprived of entertainment.

'Enjoying yourself?' he asked, coming across Lynn taking an early morning dip on the Sunday. 'I've barely seen anything of you this past week.'

'I'm having a wonderful time thanks,' she said on a light note. 'I've seen just about everything I set out to see.'

'Good.' He handed her her towel as she hoisted herself from the water, added tentatively, 'In the interests of the company, do you have any idea what Stephanos might be planning to do with the Amalia? There was some talk of his selling out the whole chain.'

Lynn shook her head. 'You'd have to ask him.'

'I can hardly do that.'

'Then let the company worry about it.' She slanted a glance. 'I can't really see what difference it makes.'

'Any change in ownership mid-season is always dodgy. We have standards to maintain.'

'But it wouldn't put you out of a job?'

'No.' He grinned suddenly. 'I just like to be up front with the news. Makes an impression with head office. I'm bucking for promotion to area rep next year when the present one leaves. Means I'd be based in Athens. Might even get to see you next year when you're passing through.'

Next year. Lynn hadn't thought that far ahead in almost a week. Her enthusiasm for the job she had coveted for so long was in no way diminished, she told herself now, just temporarily shelved. She had only these three days left before returning home. Time enough after them to start looking ahead.

'Incidentally,' Noel tagged on before sliding into the water himself, 'the island trip has been brought forward to Mondays for the rest of the season. Something to do with altered schedules. Typical of the Greeks to do it now and not at the beginning. I've pinned up a notice, but I'll have to tell everybody individually, too, in case they don't see it. Hope it doesn't mess up any plans you've already made.'

Until that moment she had totally forgotten about the trip. Her mind swiftly explored reasons for not going, but could come up with nothing that made any sense. Andreas hadn't mentioned Monday; it was quite possible he would be tied up himself after taking so much time out.

'It might be better, anyway,' she responded with determined practicality. 'Means we'll have a rest before travelling home on Wednesday.'

'There's that,' he agreed. 'See you later, maybe.'

It was still barely seven o'clock. She wasn't due to meet Andreas in the lobby until ten. Breakfast would while away an hour, but that didn't start until eight on Sundays. She could, she supposed, spend some time getting her notes into order, although she hadn't taken nearly as many here as she had in Thessaly last year.

She was still in her towelling beach wrap when the telephone shrilled just before seven-thirty. Andreas sounded lazy, as if he hadn't long been out of bed.

'I just ordered breakfast for two,' he said. 'You're not going to turn me down again, I hope?'

'I'm not dressed,' she protested after a moment. 'I went for a swim. My hair is still wet!'

'It will dry just as quickly up here as down there,' he pointed out reasonably. 'Quicker, maybe. I'm nearer the sun.'

Lynn had to laugh, knowing full well she had never had any intention of turning the invitation down. Not this time. 'Just give me a few minutes.'

It took her exactly three to shower and wriggle into her white sundress, and another two to comb her hair into sleek obedience. Apart from a splash of lipstick she could get away without make-up. Her skin was a smooth golden-brown, glowing with health and vitality. She knew she had never looked better.

The owner's apartment occupied the west corner of the top floor. Andreas greeted her in a spacious living room coolly tiled underfoot and scattered with thick Turkish rugs. There were couches and comfortably deep chairs covered in a deep blue linen and set against sparkling white walls, low carved tables scattered between. Framed paintings created vivid splashes of colour.

'All Greek artists,' he supplied as Lynn moved to study a local landscape at closer quarters.

'Your choice,' she asked, 'or your father's?'

'The interior designer's as a matter-of-fact. This is one of the bookable suites. I'm only occupying it because we don't have a reservation for it until the end of June.'

'By which time you'll be long gone?' She said it without turning.

'I should be gone now,' he admitted. 'I've reached the limit on improvements that can be done here before the end of the season.'

Did she take it she was the cause of his staying? Lynn wondered. It seemed likely considering the amount of time he was spending with her. Come Wednesday he would be free again, temptation removed. There would be other women, there was little doubt. His Greek blood coursed too strongly through his veins to stay cool for long.

'Our croissants will be going cold,' he said, surprising her because she hadn't realised that the meal had already been delivered. 'I had the table set outside on the balcony. If you'd like something more substantial I can always ring down.'

'The croissants will be fine,' Lynn assured him. 'I never eat much at breakfast.'

'A habit I never managed to acquire myself in fifteen years,' he agreed.

He led the way outside through double glass doors and saw her seated at the white-clothed table before taking his own seat. The view from up here was tremendous, the air so clear at this hour that it was possible to pick out detail on the opposite shore. The sound of laughter floated up from the pool.

They talked in a casual, easy fashion while they ate. It was almost, thought Lynn fleetingly at one point, like being married. Not that she would want to be married, to Andreas or any other man, at the present time. There was too much she still had to do with her life. It wasn't even as if she were in love with him. A month from now she would have put all this behind her.

That observation seemed to bring a new buoyancy. She sparkled with it, making him laugh with a couple of humorous little anecdotes from her London tours.

'It's no sinecure,' she acknowledged when he asked her if she was happy in her work. 'Driving in London is bad enough, parking is even worse. On shopping tours I have to drop my parties off outside the various stores and arcades, then cruise around until they're ready to carry on somewhere else, or find somewhere to wait if they're spending any length of time in one place. I suppose I could ask for a transfer to one of the group tours by coach, only if I'm going to be leaving anyway after Christmas it's hardly worthwhile.'

'You've been doing this kind of job for long?'

'Only about six months. Before that I was in a bank.'

His brows lifted. 'A pretty drastic change.'

It still surprised her at times to hear the Americanisms come so readily to his lips. She smiled and shrugged. 'I got tired of the nine-to-five routine, and I knew I was going to need a lot more than just fluency in a couple of languages to land a job with Treasury. This was just a stop-gap. If I miss out next season I'm not sure what I'll do.'

'You won't.' Andreas sounded confident of the fact. 'They'll leap at the opportunity!'

'Thanks.' The sparkle had diminished a little. She got up and went to stand at the balcony rail, looking out across the gulf to the distant hills. It was what she had wanted to hear, wasn't it? 'Where to next?' she heard herself ask. 'For you, I mean?'

'Crete, and then Rhodes,' he said. 'Leaving Kos to the end. I'm already considering offers for all three localities.'

'But you're still planning on retaining control of the Amalia?'

'Was that what your courier was asking you down at the pool earlier—or was the conversation of a more personal nature?' He had come to stand behind her, hands resting lightly on her waist as he looked over her shoulder at the same view. 'I haven't made up my mind about anything yet. I never wanted to be in this position to start with.'

She was conscious of the feel of his hands through the thin material of her dress; of the tempered strength in his grasp. His whole approach had been so circumspect this past week. Only now, feeling herself tremor to his touch, was she forced to acknowledge how desperately she wanted his lovemaking.

'What time are we supposed to be in Athens?' she heard herself asking.

'In time for lunch.' He waited, still holding her, added softly, 'We have so few days left, Lynn.'

Fewer than he thought, Lynn reflected, trying to feel grateful for small mercies. Tomorrow she would be gone for at least twelve hours. 'I have to change,' she said. 'I can't go like this.'

'You look perfect.' His lips sought the side of her neck, pressing tiny, tantalising kisses down over her bare shoulder. 'It's barely nine o'clock anyway. We don't need to leave before ten-thirty.'

'You promised.' Her voice sounded thick in her ears. 'Andreas . . .'

He let go of her with reluctance. 'It seems I misjudged the moment yet again.'

He had misjudged nothing except for her own lack

of daring, she thought wryly, torn between conflicting emotions. He knew how he affected her; he had to know. The question was whether or not she could last the distance.

CHAPTER SIX

KYRIA Stephanos lived in the Kolanaki quarter of the capitol, on the lower slopes of the Lycabettus hill. In her mid-fifties, and still retaining more than a hint of the beauty that had been hers in her youth, she spoke English almost as well as her son, although with a vastly different accent.

Her attitude towards Lynn was reserved, almost unwelcoming. Lynn thought she understood. Andreas was all she had left of her family. To have another woman usurp her place in his life would be hard for her to accept. She could have reassured her on that point, where she herself was concerned at least. In three short days she would be out of his life for good.

An opportunity to clarify the short-lived nature of their relationship came during lunch when *Kyria* Stephanos asked her how long she would be in Greece. Watching the relief revealed in the other's eyes, Lynn wondered if her reactions might have been the same had Andreas brought home a Greek girl to meet her. One of these days he was going to get married, if only to ensure the family name, although at thirty-three there was no especial hurry. Depression swamped her for a moment. Resolutely she fought it off. It was no use dwelling on what might have been. She was stuck with what was.

Andreas' suggestion that the three of them take the funicular up to the summit in order to let Lynn see the view of the city met with resistance from his parent. Only when Lynn added her own plea did she finally relent. She insisted on sitting in the rear seat of the Jaguar, despite Lynn's protests. Andreas left it to the two of them to sort out. Catching his eye as she slid into her seat, Lynn thought she registered amusement. Perhaps he thought she was being over-solicitous where his mother was concerned; trying to worm her way into her good graces. It wasn't important but it rankled. She was already regretting ever having suggested this meeting at all.

Running through a tunnel, the cable car took bare minutes to complete the ascent. The view from the top was spectacular, all of Athens spread below: white stone and marble warmed by the occasional scattering of old red tiled roofs; oases of green surrounding the relics of another age. Mountains backed the city to the north. To the south, beyond the lower heights of the Acropolis, lay the sea.

'There's Acrocorinth,' stated Andreas, pointing to the far distant horizon where more mountains edged the coastal plain. 'It isn't often clear enough to see the Peloponnese from here. They're more than fifty miles away.'

Lynn followed his direction, but was unable to pick out the exact ridge he was talking about. That day seemed a long time ago, yet little of real note had happened since. His closeness now at her side made her yearn. She had never known a man quite like him, and might never again. Only it wasn't going to happen. She couldn't allow it to happen. Forgetting him was going to be difficult enough without that.

A visit to the little chapel of St George was followed by a cool drink on the terrace of the solitary restaurant. There were surprisingly few people about for a weekend. Several tables remained unoccupied.

'You should take Lynn to visit the Parthenon at closer quarters than this,' suggested *Kyria* Stephanos.

'I already did,' returned her son. 'Last Thursday. We covered everything except this.'

'You were in Athens without coming to see me?'

'There was no time, and I knew I'd be seeing you today.'

One more black mark against her, reflected Lynn wryly, sensing the older woman's hurt. She made a mental vow that if she ever had a son of her own she would take care not to become too possessive. Easier said than done, perhaps. In *Kyria* Stephanos' circumstances she would probably feel the same.

She seized the opportunity when Andreas left the two of them alone for a few minutes to say impulsively, 'I'm sorry to have taken up so much of your son's time. He's been very good to me.'

'A man will always find time for a pretty face,' came the acrid rejoinder. There was an uncomfortable pause, then she suddenly sighed. 'You must forgive me. I am not being just. Andreas was lost to me for so many years.'

'You must have missed him terribly.'

'He was always a rebel,' the older woman admitted, responding despite herself to the sympathy. 'As the younger son he lived his life in Dion's shadow. Sending him to Canada was an attempt by his father to provide him with wider interests. I have a brother in Toronto who offered him a home for the duration of his education.'

'But he stayed beyond that.'

Faded blue eyes lifted sharply. 'He has discussed the subject with you?'

'Hardly discussed,' Lynn disclaimed. 'All I know is that he went on from university to take hotel management, and then got a job.'

'He was successful.' There was pride in the statement. 'His father could never see the difference between what he was doing there and what he would have been doing here in Greece, but I knew. What he

FREE BOOKS CERTIFICATE

Dear Susan,

Your special Introductory offer of 12 Free books is too good to miss. I understand they are mine to keep with the Free Tote Bag.

Please also reserve a Reader Service Subscription for me. If I decide to subscribe, I shall, from the beginning of the month following my free parcel of books, receive 12 new books each month for £13.20, post and packing free. If I decide not to subscribe, I shall write to you within 10 days. The free books will be mine to keep, in any case.

I understand that I may cancel my subscription at any time simply by writing to you. I am over 18 years of age.

2A6T

_____ Signature

Name _____
(BLOCK CAPITALS PLEASE)
Address _____

Postcode _____

To Susan Welland
Mills & Boon
Reader Service
FREEPOST
P.O. Box 236
CROYDON
Surrey CR9 9EL.

SEND NO MONEY NOW

had he had achieved by his own efforts.' She added sadly. 'He was not ready to leave it all behind him, even knowing that after Dion was killed, it must happen some day. Constantine never fully recovered from our loss.'

And Andreas would have been second best, and had known it, thought Lynn with a flash of understanding. Now he was stuck with the situation. He would cope though. A man like Andreas could cope with anything. She hoped she was going to be capable of doing the same come Wednesday morning.

The rest of the day passed pleasantly enough. *Kyria* Stephanos seemed to be trying to make up for her former attitude, although she showed no more than a polite regret when it came time for Lynn to say goodbye after they had all shared an early supper.

'A safe journey,' was the parting injunction, speeding her on her way, and then in Greek to her son, 'You will be here again next week?'

'I'm not sure,' he answered. 'But I'll certainly see you before I leave.' He bent to kiss her on both cheeks, adding something low toned that seemed to please her.

'That went well enough,' he observed when they were in the car. 'I haven't tried taking anyone with me before.'

'I think she probably liked me well enough as a person,' said Lynn with apparent carelessless, 'but she feared the worst.'

His glance shifted sideways fleetingly. 'Being?'

'Losing you to another woman.' Lynn kept her tone light. 'Luckily I was able to set her mind at rest on that score.'

'You were?' His expression was unrevealing. 'When?'

'You were there. At lunch, when she asked me how long I'd be in Greece.'

'Oh, that?' He was silent while he negotiated a busy junction, carrying on as if there had been no break in the conversation the moment they were clear. 'Hardly conclusive, was it?'

'With two thousand miles between us we're hardly going to be seeing each other again.'

'Closer to fifteen hundred,' he corrected.

The comment rattled her. 'Don't split hairs. You should have told her I was just a passing acquaintance in the first place. It would have saved her a lot of uncertainty.'

'No.' It was Andreas' turn to shorten his tone. 'Much as I think of her, I refuse to allow her to influence my life to the point where I dare do nothing for fear of upsetting her. I couldn't take being possessed by any woman, much less my own mother!'

'Meaning you'd expect total freedom of choice even if you married one?'

'We're not talking about the same things,' he said. 'Tomorrow I thought we . . .'

'I'm going on the island trip.' She was looking out through the windscreen at a sky brushed with mauve and orange and green as the day slowly died. 'It was arranged the first day here.'

'You can get out of it.'

Sheer determination forced the lie from her lips. 'I don't want to get out of it.'

'I see.' There was a pause, then he shrugged. 'It isn't all that important. You'll be having an early start, I imagine?'

Lynn grimaced. 'Breakfast at six.'

'Then my plans for the rest of this evening had better be cancelled, too.'

Her head came round. 'What plans?'

'I thought to take you to one of the inland villages,' he said. 'A little more authentic atmosphere. You'll need an early night if you're going to be up with the dawn.'

There was little use pointing out that she would be sitting down for several hours until they got to Hydra, Lynn reflected wryly. She had made the choice and he had accepted it. What more did she want from him?'

It was barely ten when they reached the Amalia, but he made no attempt to detain her. Thanking him for the day, Lynn wished she had the guts to say she had changed her mind about tomorrow. There were too many people around to exchange kisses, even if he had had any intentions in that direction. She felt deprived for lack of contact with that muscular body. There was every chance that he might not bother with her Tuesday, either, after this. Moving away was one of the hardest things she had done in her life.

The trill of the alarm call she had booked brought her reluctantly awake at five-thirty. Resolutely, she showered and got into white shorts and sleeveless top, slid her feet into comfortable sandals and went downstairs to join the rest of the party. The Downings, she was thankful to note, were not present.

On the coach she found herself seated with a middle-aged woman from London whose husband had elected to stay behind because he wasn't a good sailor. Noel was involved in sorting out his paperwork for the greater part of the journey, although he found time to come back and exchange a few words.

'Should have done it last night,' he admitted ruefully when Lynn commented on his work load. 'Too much candle burning, that's my trouble!'

'And Wednesday you start all over again,' she said, trying to sound sympathetic.

'That's right.' He didn't appear too downcast by the the thought. 'I thought you might have backed out today,' he added on a bland note. 'Other commitments, and all that.'

Lynn smiled. 'After paying out all those drachma?'

'Just a thought. Anyway, hope you enjoy it now you're here.'

Lynn hoped so, too. She needed some consolation.

Some caught up on their sleep over the following hour. Wide awake by now, Lynn spent most of the time looking out of the window at a landscape already familiar. This had to be about the sixth time she had covered this route, she reckoned. A week from now she would be back at work, or almost. Andreas aside, she was going to miss the Greek scene. Hopefully, it wouldn't be for long, though. If all went as planned, she should be already well into her first season at this time next year.

There was a seeming chaos of arriving and departing coaches at the docks. Noel handed out sailing tickets at the doorway, repeating that the coach would be there when they landed again at seven-thirty to take them back to the Amalia.

The island ferry was much larger than Lynn had somehow imagined it would be, and it was already crowded. Clutching her canvas tote bag, she lined up with the rest to mount the gangway, eyes lifting to idly scan the sea of faces at the rail above and freeze in sudden disbelief. Andreas raised a hand in acknowledgement. He was smiling, dark head tilted quizzically. Lynn felt her spirits start to soar, the whole day to take on new zest. Heartache to come or not, he was here right now and that was all that mattered.

He met her at the head of the gangway, pushing his way through the throng to take her elbow. 'Come for'ard,' he said. 'There's more chance of finding a seat.'

When they did it was on a crate, but she didn't care. 'When did you decide to come?' she asked. 'And why not on the coach with the rest of us? There were several spare seats.'

He laughed, shaking his head. 'I wanted to surprise you.'

'You certainly did that.' She added softly, 'I thought you'd given up on me.'

His eyes roved her hair and face, the spark glowing deep. 'Not a chance. Why else would I still be here and not in Crete where I should be?' He bent forward and kissed her on the lips, ignoring the glances and comments from those around them. 'We have today and tomorrow. After that . . .' He paused, brow tilting. 'Who knows?'

Right now Lynn had no thought for the future. It was enough to be sitting here with him. She felt so vibrantly alive.

It was over two hours sailing time to Hydra, their first port of call. The harbour was crowded with craft of all shapes and sizes, the whole picturesque town dominated by the barren crags at its back. Shops and *tavernas* alike were doing brisk business along the waterfront.

With barely an hour and a half before their boat left again, Lynn was happy enough to settle for a stroll along the quayside.

'It's more commercialised than I hoped,' she said on a regretful note over an iced drink. 'I suppose it's inevitable.'

'It's too near the mainland to be anything else,' Andreas agreed. 'All these day trippers don't help.'

'Like us?' She looked at him ruefully. 'It isn't the kind of trip you'd take by choice, is it?'

He smiled and shrugged. 'No, but what does that have to do with anything? I'm here because you're here. I've seen the rest of the scenery before.'

'I feel guilty,' she admitted. 'You had other plans for today.' She paused, waiting, wrinkling her nose at him when he failed to make the anticipated reply. 'You're not going to tell me what they were?'

'I planned to take you up into the mountains. There's a medieval castle at Karitaena. Off the regular tourist track, but worth seeing just for its own sake.' He was watching her face. 'We could always go tomorrow if you're interested.'

She was, though not especially in ancient remains. Every hour spent with Andreas was a bonus. Her smile was bright. 'I'd like that.' She started as the blast of a ship's siren rent the air, glancing at her watch. 'There's the signal we were told to listen for. Shouldn't we be going?'

'We still have a few minutes,' said Andreas, undisturbed. 'Finish your drink.'

They made it back to the ship just before the gangway was lifted. An Italian couple had claimed their crate, leaving them with little alternative but to prop themselves against the rail as the island receded.

'One down, two to go,' joked Lynn with the same rueful inflection. 'Do you think you can take it?'

Andreas put an arm about her shoulders, drawing her close to his side where she could feel the warmth of his body. His lips were light at her temple, a caress more than a kiss. 'We could stay the rest of the day on Poros,' he suggested, 'then take the hydrofoil back to Piraeus. It's been a long time since I was there, but I can remember a back-street *taverna* where the *souvlakia* was unsurpassed!'

The temptation was strong. With three islands to fit in, there was going to be little time to see very much of any of them—a detail that hadn't previously occurred to her. 'What about the coach?' she asked hesitantly. 'Noel won't have the right head count.'

'We'll find one of your party and ask them to pass on the message.' Andreas was obviously not about to allow minor problems to stand in the way. 'We can rent mopeds and ride out along the coast—perhaps take a bathe in the sea.'

'I didn't bring a costume,' she said.

'Neither did I if it comes to that, but there are plenty of shops around the harbour.' Voice teasing, he added, 'Those scraps you women wear can't possibly cost a great deal.'

Little did he know, thought Lynn, recalling the exorbitant price she had paid for her own particular scraps. Still, with the money she had saved this past week, she could well afford to splash out. The mental pun made her smile. Today, almost anything could make her smile.

'So we jump ship,' she agreed recklessly.

Where Hydra had been bare volcanic rock, Poros was clothed in green beyond the town itself, her inland hills thickly wooded. The harbour was a vast, almost landlocked lake facing the mainland and affording a fine view of the Peloponnesian mountains. Kimomeni, Andreas called them, explaining that it meant Sleeping Woman. He traced out the shape for her with an expressive hand, conjuring up the thrusting breasts, the curve of belly and hip, the tapering legs. Not given to all to perceive on first sight, he acknowledged amusedly when Lynn claimed she couldn't form the picture.

They found a shop selling beach wear among other things along the waterfront, but decided to leave any purchasing until after lunch. The backstreet *taverna* Andreas remembered was still there, and still under the same management. The proprietor himself came to greet them when he sent in his name, stocky body shaking with real emotion as he clasped the younger man by the arms.

'So long you've been away,' he cried. 'So long since you were here in my house! For you I do a special dish!'

Andreas was laughing, not in the least embarrassed by the attention they were drawing. 'All we want is to taste your *souvlakia*, Stavros. I've been singing its praises all morning.'

Shrewd old eyes turned Lynn's way, examining her from head to foot with immediate and unconcealed approval. 'This is your woman?'

'I'm just a tourist,' she said in Greek before Andreas could answer that one. She smiled at the man. 'A very hungry one!'

He was galvanised into instant action. 'Five minutes,' he promised. 'No more!'

Andreas was watching her, mouth faintly curved. '*Are* you my woman?' he asked softly.

Her stomach lurched as she met the knowledgeable dark eyes. 'You tell me,' was all she could manage to say.

'If it's up to me the answer has to be yes.' The smile had spread to his eyes, sparkling them with dancing lights. '*Yineka*.'

Yineka. It meant my wife as well as my woman. She felt her heart jerk at the single blast of the horn from the harbour, but she made no move. It was already too late.

The *souvlakia* was every bit as good as Andreas had said. They had double helpings, washed down with copious draughts of Domestica. For Lynn the wine had a dual purpose in that it not only quenched her thirst but relaxed her into the bargain. This day was special; let it bring what it would. Nothing bad could happen to her while she was with Andreas.

It was still only a little after two-thirty when they finished. Walking at Andreas' side, with her hand clasped lightly in his, Lynn felt on top of the world. They had hours of daylight left in which to hire the promised cycles and find a beach. First though, they had to buy the swimwear. That shouldn't take long now they knew where to look for it.

The sound of her name shouted from one of the boats berthed alongside the wharf came as a shock, the sight of Sue's curly red-brown head even more so. She summoned a smile to her lips as Tim joined his girlfriend on deck.

'Hi there! I thought you two were miles away by now.'

'We've been laid up for repairs,' Sue advised. 'The engine went kaput.' Her eyes went from Lynn to Andreas, curiosity apparent. 'Hello.'

Lynn performed introductions, only realising when she was halfway through them that she had no idea of either Tim or Sue's surnames. Not that it mattered, she supposed. 'Friends of Noel's,' she finished.

'Stephanos?' repeated the other girl. 'Are you the same one who owns the Amalia?'

Andreas inclined his head. 'I didn't realise I was that well known.'

'Noel mentioned the name a couple of times,' she said lightly. 'Did you come in on the hydrofoil, or do you have your own boat?'

It was Andreas who answered. 'We arrived on the tour ferry but decided not to go on to Aegina.'

'Don't blame you.' She added brightly, 'Look, why don't you come aboard and have a drink with us?'

'We've just finished lunch,' Lynn put in a little too fast. 'We were planning to go for a swim along the coast.'

'So were we.' Obviously Sue didn't take hints. 'The best bits of beach can only be reached from the sea. There's one we've found less than twenty minutes away that's nearly all sand. We'd be glad to take you along with us, wouldn't we, Tim?'

'Sure.' The latter was easy. 'Climb aboard.'

Lynn tried again, wishing Andreas would say

something. 'We didn't bring any bathing things. We were on our way to buy some.'

'Oh, don't bother about that.' Sue ran an expert eye over Andreas' hipline. 'Tim's spare trunks should fit you okay, and bikinis are pretty adaptable.'

'In that case there's nothing to stop us.' Andreas put a hand behind Lynn's waist, urging her forward. 'Let's go.'

If it was what he wanted she wasn't going to argue about it, Lynn thought, trying to conceal her own reluctance. She didn't understand his apparent eagerness to share today with anyone else. It wasn't the impression he had given earlier.

All the same, she had to admit to enjoying the trip along the coast in the balmy afternoon breeze. Andreas appeared to be in his element. As Tim was moved to remark, he certainly knew about boats.

'I was a member of a yacht club in Toronto,' he supplied casually. 'There are several on the lake.'

'You had your own boat?' asked Tim.

'For the last three years I was there, yes.'

'What class?'

Sue touched Lynn's arm. 'Let's go down and change while we have the chance.'

Once below, she fished out the bottom half of a yellow-and-white cotton bikini, tossing it across. 'Not exactly new, I'm afraid, but beggars can't be choosers. You're slimmer round the hips than I am so you'll have to tighten the strings.'

Lynn said uncomfortably, 'Do you have the top half?'

'Oh, nobody bothers round here. I haven't myself these last few days.' She looked at Lynn's face, then shrugged good-humouredly and rooted again through the locker. 'I suppose it must in here somewhere— yep, here it is. You won't mind if I don't?'

'Not at all.' It was an outright lie because it was going to make her feel just as conspicuous if in a different sense, but there was no other answer she could make. Even if she could have brought herself to appear half naked in front of Andreas again knowing his views on that kind of provocation, she certainly wouldn't be prepared to do it with a man she barely knew there too.

Sue apparently suffered no such self-consciousness. She had a good figure, Lynn was bound to admit. She watched for Andreas' reaction when the two of them went back on deck, but neither man paid much attention, intent on bringing the boat in round the little headland to anchor off a tiny crescent of beach backed by solid rock. The sea certainly looked the only possible approach.

It was wonderfully warm in the water, the latter so clear every rock was visible. Lynn made for the little beach after a while, lying down her back with eyes closed against the sun's rays. Andreas came to join her, propping himself on an elbow as he trickled sand on to her bare stomach.

'I'm glad you kept your top on,' he said. 'Was it because of me or the company?'

'Both,' she admitted, still without opening her eyes. 'I told you last time, I only did it at all because I thought I was alone. Sue can get away with it because she thinks nothing of it.'

'Sue,' he said drily, 'is very much aware of herself, believe me. You said they were friends of your courier's. How did you meet them yourself?'

'He took me down to Portochellon the first Sunday. It seems ages ago now.' She rolled her head a little to look at him, taking in the lean strength of his features, the sheer sensuality in the lines of his mouth. Droplets of water still beaded his shoulders and arms and upper thighs, arousing an urge in her to lean forward and lick them off. She licked her lips instead, abruptly desisting as she caught his eye. 'Why did you want to come with them?' she heard herself ask.

His shrug made light of the question. 'It was as good a way as any of passing the afternoon. Wherever we went, there were likely to be other people around.'

So it wasn't because he had changed his mind about wanting to be alone with her. Lynn's spirits took a lift, only to plunge once more at the realisation that this was all there was going to be. Without stopping to think about it, she put out a hand and touched his chest, running a finger tip down through the damp tangle of hair to the hard ridge of muscle above his waistband with ears tuned to the roughened intake of his breath. He covered the hand with one of his, pressing it between them as he rolled to find her mouth, lips demanding, pressuring hers open, his tongue a subtle torment. He was already aroused; the brief swimtrunks made no secret of that. Lynn stiffened as he thrust a knee between hers, suddenly recalling where they were.

'The others!' she murmured. 'Andreas!'

He stopped at once, revealing by his rueful expression that he had forgotten the onlookers, too. 'I was carried away,' he admitted, easing his weight from her.

The other couple were still in the water. Tim had his back to the shore, but Sue was looking their way. She made no attempt to hide the fact either, lifting a hand in a cheeky thumbs up sign before disappearing beneath the surface.

'I made a mistake' Andreas said softly. 'We should have kept to the original plan.' His eyes moved over her, lingering on the silky smoothness of her thighs. 'You're still quivering,' he observed. 'I know how you feel. Another moment or two and there would have been no stopping.' He paused, gaze coming back to her face, his look kindling fresh flames inside her. 'It has to happen, Lynn. We both of us want it to happen.'

'How?' Her voice was a whisper. 'There's so little time left.'

One lean hand caressed her cheek. 'Leave it to me.'

She sat up suddenly, too tense to take any more. 'I'm going back in,' she said. 'Are you coming?'

'In a little while.' His smile held an element of irony. 'I need a few minutes to recover my equilibrium, as you might say. Go ahead. I'll catch you up.'

The water felt cooler this time. She struck out immediately for the boat, finding some relief in the physical exertion. Leave it to him, Andreas had said, though exactly what he had in mind she wasn't sure. She wanted him to make love to her, there was no doubt about that. What concerned her was the way she was going to feel afterwards. Deny it she might, but she was more than a little emotionally involved. And that was something she was going to have to work out for herself.

Sue came back on board while she was still drying herself, stretching out like a cat on top of the cabin superstructure to soak up the sun, her red-brown curls flattened to her shapely head.

'Just a holiday affair?' she asked casually. 'Or is there more to it than that?'

'It isn't an affair,' Lynn denied. 'Not the way you mean, at any rate.'

'There are other kinds?' Her tone was amused. 'Come on, you're not that naïve! You weren't exactly holding back on the beach just now.'

It was odd, Lynn reflected, how different people

could turn out to be from first impressions. Last week she had liked Sue; today she found her objectionable. She strove to keep her temper battened down. The fault had been her own in encouraging Andreas to touch her at all while they were on public view.

'What time were you planning on getting back to the harbour?' she asked. 'We have to catch the hydrofoil back to Piraeus. I'm not sure when the last one is.'

This time the other did take the hint, seemingly without rancour. 'It's up to you two. Once the men come back on board there's nothing to stop us.'

Lynn glanced shorewards, relieved to see both heads not too far distant. 'They're on their way now.'

'Then we should be there by six, allowing for the wind. It was behind us coming.'

'Can't you use the engine?'

'Can't afford to waste the juice except in emergencies. The repairs cost a bomb. I wanted to have the engine overhauled properly before we sailed this season, but Tim was sure it would last out. He doesn't remember saying it, of course. Men are dab hands at forgetting what they don't want to admit.' Sue sat up to run her fingers through her rapidly drying hair, tanned body lithe as a twenty-year-old's. 'I fancy a long cold drink, if that fridge of ours can be persuaded to part with some ice. How about you?'

'Sounds good,' Lynn agreed, already regretting her former assessment. Sue simply said what she thought; there was no real malice in her.

Andreas was first over the side. Seated aft, Lynn met his eyes and registered the leap in her pulse rate. She allowed her gaze to drift down the length of his hard muscled torso as he half turned away to reach for a towel, lingering a fraction too long in the region of his loins so that he caught her at it. His slow smile

mocked her swift flush, though not unkindly. Later,
his look seemed to say.

They were back at the quayside for a little after six
o'clock. Sue made no serious attempt to detain them.
Lynn waited until they were well clear of the boat
before asking about the hydrofoil. They had plenty of
time, Andreas assured her. Supper was the first
consideration.

The *tavernas* were just beginning to serve meals
again, mostly to tourists at this hour. Lynn had
expected to go back to Stavros', but instead Andreas
chose a place right on the waterfront where they could
watch the comings and goings as afternoon merged
into evening and the locals began to emerge from their
daytime retreats.

The light was golden, the vivid sky of afternoon
dissolving now into a softer, misty blue as the day
slowly died. Eating in Greece was never a business to
be hurried. One relaxed and waited, nibbling at a salad
and imbibing the local wine while savoury smells
tantalised the taste buds. All along the waterfront the
hustle and bustle of commerce was quietening, giving
way to a gentler, less acquisitive atmosphere as the
tourists and day trippers thinned out. The fading
thunder of a departing hydrofoil left a relative if not
yet total peace in its wake.

'I've been toying with the idea of buying property
here for the winter,' he remarked casually. 'I always
did like the place.'

Lynn glanced at him. 'I'd have thought Athens
more your style.'

'Which goes to prove how little you know me.' His
smiled robbed the words of any real sting but they still
left an ache in her throat. 'In any case,' he added, 'it's
close enough to the mainland.

She said tentatively, 'Would your mother come, too?'

He shook his head. 'Even if the idea appealed to me, she wouldn't want to leave the friends she has in Kalonaki. I'd still see her every weekend.'

She would willingly settle for that much herself, Lynn thought. For the first time in days, and for no apparent reason, her sister's name came to mind, drawing the next question from her without volition. 'You haven't considered returning to Canada at all?'

Dark brows drew together as he studied her. 'There's no question of it. Why such interest in Canada?'

It was Lynn's turn to shake her head. It was too late now to start delving into that matter. 'No special reason.'

'Just making conversation for the sake of it?' The frown vanished, replaced by a look that made her tremble inwardly. He took her hand, raising it to his lips to lightly kiss her fingertips. 'Stay with me,' he murmured. 'Here on Poros. I want you, *ylikia.*'

For a wild moment she actually thought he meant permanently, but only for a moment. Later, he had said, and this was later. Perhaps he had planned it this way from the start. It scarcely mattered because she knew she wasn't going to say no. She had known all afternoon.

CHAPTER SEVEN

THE sun was setting, turning the sky to molten orange-red, the sea to burnished pewter. He read her answer in her eyes, his response immediate and warming.

'Now we have time and to spare,' he said. 'A whole night.'

And no regrets, she thought resolutely. This was one time she was going to cast aside petty restrictions. She didn't ask where they would stay; the detail would be taken care of.

Lamps were lit as darkness gathered, each table supplied with a candle contained within a glass bowl. Windows began twinkling across the lake and on the mainland. The rest of her party would be on the coach and heading for home by now, Lynn realised. She had no desire to be with them, nor even any concern about what might be thought.

Bouzouki music came from a speaker on the *taverna* wall, setting the feet dancing with its emotive rhythm. A couple of the waiters took time off from serving the customers to do the *sirtaki*, arms wrapped about each other's shoulders, bodies moving in near perfect unison as they bent and leapt energetically through the steps.

No sooner had they retired than three burly, unshaven men dressed in open-necked shirts and rough working trousers moved on to the floor, two of them squatting with rhythmically clicking fingers while the other expressed his mood of the moment in a lusty performance that was more than a little suggestive in its gestures and postures and drew a roar of approbation from the surrounding tables. The *rebitika*, Andreas called it, joining in the applause. He looked more Greek than he had ever looked tonight, Lynn thought, hair jet black in the lamplight, eyes sparkling like coals. This was the real Andreas, shorn of his Western sophistication and enjoying himself the way only the Greeks could. If this feeling he roused in her wasn't love then it had to be the closest thing to it.

It was gone eleven before he made any move to leave. His arm was about her shoulders as they strolled the length of the waterfront, warm and possessive. There were others taking the same parade, or sitting in voluble family groups at *taverna* tables; music came from all sides. The faint breeze stirred Lynn's hair at the temples, bringing with it the scent of lemons. She wondered idly what it would be like here in winter. Certainly it would never get really cold. People might spend a little more time indoors but life would follow much the same pattern.

She had suspected all along where they would be spending the night and she wasn't disappointed. Stavros was still doing brisk business, the two live *bouzouki* players an obvious draw.

Andreas led the way round to the side of the building where a flight of concrete stairs gave access to the upper floor. A single corridor had doors opening off it either side. He selected the second one on the right, standing back to allow her to enter ahead of him, his smile plucking at her heartstrings. He had to have arranged all this at lunchtime, yet Lynn couldn't bring herself to care too much. The decision had been hers to make.

Apart from the double bed, the room held little in the way of furniture, but it smelled fresh and clean. Window shutters filtered the light from the street lamp outside into slatted bars across the plain white coverlet. Andreas closed the door again softly behind him and took her into his arms, kissing away the last lingering doubts. She clung to him when he lifted her to take her across to the bed, feeling the roughness of his jawline against her lips. They were lacking almost every refinement for a night away from home but it didn't matter. Tomorrow could take care of itself.

He undressed her without haste, mouth tender as he kissed her ears, her lips, her eyes, his hands bringing every part of her body to vibrant life. It took him bare seconds to shed his own clothing, then he was there at her side, turning her towards him to hold her close against his hard length, making her aware of his readiness yet still intent on giving her pleasure first.

His was the first male body Lynn had ever explored in any detail; the first she had ever felt the desire to know with such intimacy. She let her fingers rove where they willed, feeling him quiver to her touch, hearing the sharp intake of his breath; knowing the sweetness of her own power to provide. They were attuned to each other, sensing every need.

She knew the moment when he could hold out no longer because she felt the same. The weight of him pinioned her, spreading her limbs in supple surrender. There was no thought, no other sensation but this fire inside her and the wild ecstasy racing through her veins.

It was still dark when she awoke and for a moment she was disorientated. Only when her hand touched the hard male thigh thrown across her did her memory supply the detail. Andreas stirred and shifted, but the leg and arm were not withdrawn. What was his remained his, even in his sleep.

She wanted him again, that much she knew for sure.

Her body felt tensed with the longing. Making love with Andreas was a total experience; a sensual feast. She knew things about herself she had never acknowledged before—things she had been too inhibited to acknowledge. With Andreas there was nothing she couldn't do, nothing she couldn't say—except for those three little words even now nibbling at the edge of her mind. It wasn't love he wanted from her; not that kind anyway. In another two days they would say goodbye and he would forget her. She couldn't blame anyone but herself. She had known the risks.

As if in direct response to her thoughts, he stirred again, murmuring something beneath his breath as he started to waken. One hand slid up from her waist to cover her breast with the familiarity natural to a man not unaccustomed to wakening up with a woman by his side, fingers curving to her shape.

Lynn lay immobile. The word had been indistinct, true, but her ears were finely tuned. Caroline, he had said. If she had doubted before she could hardly do it now. Six months, and he still dreamed about her. But then why had he left her that way? Why hadn't he contacted her since? Because she was married? Because he hadn't realised how she felt about him? Anything was possible, none of it comforting. She was in bed with her sister's former lover. That fact alone was enough to contend with.

Her rigidity got through to him, bringing him fully awake. 'What is it?' he asked softly.

'Nothing.' She had to force the word out. His hand was still on her breast. She pushed it away, tagging on jerkily, 'I just don't feel like being handled, that's all.'

He lifted himself on an elbow the better to see her. Dawn light was beginning to filter through the shutters, revealing his features in dim outline. The lift of his eyebrow was expressive. 'That doesn't sound like the woman I fell asleep with.'

'That was then, this is now.' Lynn wanted to get up, to get away from him, but he was too close, his leg still pinning her calves. The feel of his body against her brought words tumbling from her lips. 'You had what you were after, isn't that enough?'

Dim though the light was, it was sufficient to see the sudden blanking out of all expression from his eyes and face. For a long moment he just lay there looking at her, then he shrugged and rolled away on to his back. 'I'm sure you're right,' he said indifferently. 'We already exhausted the potential. Go back to sleep. I shan't disturb you again.'

Sleep was farthest from her mind. She wanted to scream at him, to hammer at his callous back. She had said it, yes, but she hadn't meant it. Last night had been more than just a physical experience.

For her perhaps, came the cold voice of reason, obviously not for him. He was even capable of ignoring his own physiological responses if it meant going to any effort of pretence. She had known all along of his lack of emotional commitment; provoking him into confirming it was like sticking pins into herself. She could have tried telling him the truth as an alternative. At least that would have retained her some advantage.

She knew why she hadn't, of course. She had been afraid to put theory to test—to learn that his feelings for Caro had been any different. She was jealous of her own sister, that's what it boiled down to. She always had been jealous, if not for the same reasons. All those ideas about making Andreas pay for what he had done to her had been an excuse. She had wanted to be with him for her own sake. Well, it was over now. And perhaps as well. If she kept on telling herself that she might eventually come to believe it.

She must have slept again in the end because the next time she opened her eyes it was broad daylight. The screens had been folded back from the windows, letting in the fresh morning air along with a slanting shaft from a sun not yet over the rooftops.

Viewing the empty bed at her side, Lynn wondered numbly if Andreas had walked out and left her to make her own way back to the mainland. It didn't seem unlikely considering his attitude earlier. Lucky she had some *drachma* with her because yesterday's ticket was no longer valid.

Even as she sat up, the door opened and he came in. He was fully dressed in the lightweight slacks and shirt, and was carrying a parcel which he tossed on to the bed.

'Towels,' he said briefly. 'Plus toothpaste and brushes and disposable razor for me. There's soap already in the bathroom along the corridor. We may as well start the day in a civilised fashion.'

Lynn reached out and unfastened the paper bag, taking care to keep the sheet tucked under her arms. Ridiculous it might be, but the circumstances were vastly different now. She felt cheap and self-conscious and not a little ashamed. Her own clothes lay across the only chair in the room, neatly folded and quite beyond reach. The obvious thing was to ask Andreas to pass them across, only the words stuck in her throat. She couldn't even bring herself to look at him.

He solved the problem by taking the things he needed from her, the touch of his fingers quite impersonal. 'I'll go first,' he said. 'Wrap the sheet round you if it means that much.'

She had to glance up then, registering the faint lift at the corner of his upper lip. The dark eyes were impenetrable. It was difficult to believe that last night had ever happened. Could she possibly have lain in this man's arms; felt the intimate intrusion of his body? She knew her colour was rising and could do nothing about it.

Only when the door had closed behind him did she stir herself to move. The sheet was thin enough to wind round and tuck in, although it trailed on the floor. From the window she could see the length of the narrow street below. An old man was leading a loaded donkey along it. At one end there was a glimpse of wooded hills, while the other gave on to one of the wider thoroughfares running down towards the waterfront. The sounds reaching her ears confirmed that the day was already well under way.

Tomorrow at this time she would be eating breakfast in readiness for the journey to the airport. The way she felt now it couldn't come soon enough. There was an urge in her to throw on her clothes and leave the place before Andreas came back, but it was hardly practical. Somehow she had to find the nerve to see this thing through to the bitter end.

He made it easier for her by simply stopping by to tell her he had finished, then continuing on down the stairs. The bathroom was very basic, with a roughly tiled shower tray instead of a bath. Andreas had left his towel over the rail. Lynn did the same. Stavros no doubt would find a use for them. There was no mirror, so she returned to the bedroom to use the cracked one over the chest of drawers in order to comb her hair and apply lipstick. Her eyes had a bruised look. She avoided searching them too deeply. Everything passed in time, she told herself with emphasis. It was the only comfort she could find.

Andreas had taken a table out front under the canvas and was drinking coffee. He pulled out a chair for her when he saw her coming, indicating the earthenware coffee pot and spare cup. 'Help yourself. There's food on its way.'

'I'm not hungry,' she said, pouring the coffee with a surprisingly steady hand. 'This will be enough for me.' She took a moment or two before asking, 'What time is the first hydrofoil back to Athens?'

'About fifteen minutes after the first one arrives.' His tone was sardonic. 'I already arranged for a fast trip back with one of the speedboat owners. You'll be at the Amalia in time for lunch.'

'Good.' It was all she could think of to say.

The silence stretched between them. Andreas was the first to break it. 'If I'd told you last night that I loved you would your attitude this morning be any different?'

Lynn made herself meet his eyes, responding to the irony with a curl of her own lip. 'Not the slightest.'

'Then what the devil *is* wrong with you?' he exploded. 'You didn't do any holding back that I noticed.'

Lynn winced inwardly but kept a level tone. 'You said it yourself. We exhausted the potential.'

'And that's a reason for turning surly on me earlier?'

'I wasn't surly,' she denied. 'Just not interested in repetition. I'm sorry if your *philotimos* suffers.

There was a dangerous glint in the dark eyes. 'No woman—especially a non-Greek—can conceive what the word truly means. Drink your coffee. We'll leave as soon as we're both finished.'

They reached the Amalia at noon. Lynn lost no time in going upstairs to change, seizing the opportunity while she was in her room to pack the majority of her things. One more night to get through and then home. She could hardly wait.

The journey here had been strained to say the least. Andreas had barely said a word. In some respects she regretted the way she had handled the situation, yet what alternative had there been? Even if she could have brought herself to ask him about Caro it would have involved so many explanations, and still not shown herself in a very good light. The only thing she could do now was forget him. Simple enough to say, not so easy to do, but she had no choice. From the way he had left her just now, she wouldn't be seeing him again before she departed the premises anyway.

She spent a lazy afternoon topping up her tan at the poolside. Noel discovered her there around four.

'You got back okay then?' he observed superfluously, laying his towel next to hers. 'I was beginning to wonder if you'd make the plane tomorrow.'

Lynn stayed where she was on her front with her chin resting on bent forearms. 'There was never any question of it.'

He digested that for a moment before saying softly, 'Matters a lot, does it?'

Something inside her stiffened, dragging the sharp retort from her. 'I don't think your position entitles you to ask.' She caught herself up almost in the same instant, turning her head to look at him with a wry expression. 'Sorry. That was a nasty crack. I'm feeling a bit liverish.'

His shrug made light of the moment. 'You're right, anyway. I'm supposed to remain objective at all times.' He hesitated briefly. 'Look, I'll be finished here mid-October. I know that's a whole five months away, but I'd like to see you when I get back to London. How about it?'

Any reminder of this place and time was going to be unwelcome the way she felt right now, Lynn considered, yet five months was a long time. Noel was good company and she liked him. He could also, she was bound to acknowledge, be very helpful. That job next season was all she cared about.

'Why not?' she said. 'Give me a call when you do get back.'

'I'll need your number.' He jotted it down on a scrap of paper torn from a magazine someone had left, and knotted it into the corner of his towel. 'The only trouble with swimming gear,' he remarked. 'Nowhere to carry anything.' He collapsed again into a prone position with a sigh of contentment. 'Another hour before I need think about moving. What are you doing tonight?'

'Not a lot,' she admitted.

'Then perhaps you'll come on down to the disco with me for a final fling?'

She glanced at him sideways. 'What about your redhead?'

He grimaced. 'She's been playing me off against a couple of waiters.'

Which probably meant he wanted to show her there were more fish in the sea, Lynn reflected. Well, that was all right. 'Why not?' she said again, giving herself no further time to think about it. At the very least it would make the time go faster.

Just about the whole of the British contingent appeared to have had the same idea regarding the evening's entertainment. Already acquainted with most from the night of the silver wedding celebrations, Lynn found little opportunity for brooding.

None of those due to leave in the morning were eager to retire. They kept the disc jockey going way beyond his scheduled closing time. Lynn finally extricated herself around 1.30, leaving Noel dancing cheek to cheek with his forgiving and obviously forgiven redhead. She felt no resentment. Tomorrow she would be gone, but the other girl was here for a further week. Noel was simply getting his priorities in order.

Her room, as usual, was too warm for comfort. She took the small easy chair out on to the balcony and sat listening to the sounds of revelry still coming from below. She wasn't in the least bit tired, she had to admit. Just too restless to take any more communal jollity at close quarters. Her own tiny flat was going to seem like a haven after a fortnight of this.

It hadn't all been the same though, had it? came the thought. Andreas had been an excellent companion. An undemanding companion until the latter end, too, yet she had known all along where his forebearance was leading. Last night at this time they had been in bed together, asleep in each other's arms. If she had stayed asleep, or her ears weren't quite so sharp, they might be together now. Yet what difference would it have made come the morning? The parting had to happen whatever the circumstances. To Andreas she had been no more than a passing challenge. She may have dented his male pride a little but that was all. In a week he would have forgotten her name.

Gradually the night became quiet as the last of the merry-makers conceded defeat. The cicadas themselves were muted by the pleasantly cooling air. From where she sat, Lynn could see an edge of the pool, still water reflecting the starlight. A swim might relax her and enable her to get some sleep. Some rest was advisable before the long journey home.

She got up and went to put on a bikini, covering herself with her beach robe and not bothering with a towel. Just a few lengths and she would come straight back up.

There was no one on the desk when she went through the lobby. The terrace lights had all been turned off, but the moon was high enough to show the paved pathway in sufficient detail. Lynn felt adventurous, even a little audacious being out here on her own at this hour of the morning.

Stripping off her robe, she slid silently into the

water and began a calm, unhurried breaststroke down the length of the pool, turning at the far end to continue the same easy rhythm. She didn't bother to count; that wasn't the point of the exercise. When she tired she would stop.

She had been swimming for some ten minutes or so and was coming up to the turn in the shallow end when she became aware that someone else was in the water with her. Hard hands seized her, bringing her round and upright before jerking her closer to a body all too familiar. Andreas was naked; that much Lynn discovered in the first few seconds of contact. His mouth seared hers, forcefully parting her lips. She felt her back come up against the side of the pool, preventing any escape as his hands left her hips to bare her breasts to his ruthless exploration—felt the sudden flaring response run through her.

Helplessly, she began kissing him back, sensing the change in him, the gradual modification of intent until he was making love to her rather than at her, mouth softened, cherishing hers with slow sensuality, his hands rediscovering her most intimate secrets.

She wanted him so badly she could scarcely contain the need. The water cushioned the two of them, cool and caressing in its gentle lap as their bodies joined, became one—prolonging the fervour to a point where all sense of time or place or even reason dissolved into mist.

Andreas was first out of the pool, hauling her to a seat on the edge beside him. His eyes were questioning as he looked at her.

'So *now* tell me why,' he said. 'The real reason you turned against me this morning.'

Her own glance flickered away to the crumpled heap that was his silk robe nearby. He must have bided his time until he was out of her line of vision on that last length. 'How did you know I was down here?' she asked, putting her thoughts into words in an instinctive bid to gain time.

'I was out on my balcony when you went in. I couldn't be totally sure it was you in the dark but it was worth a chance.' He paused, waiting, shaking his head when she failed to respond. 'You're not leaving here till you satisfy me, Lynn.'

Her mouth curved faintly. 'I thought I'd just done that.'

'Don't prevaricate.' He wasn't amused. 'The fact that you did simply underlines the question. Why pretend? Was it some kind of game you were playing?'

'If I said yes would you accept it?' She made a rueful little gesture as his mouth tautened. 'All right, it was no game. I can't imagine anyone doing that anyway.'

'You'd be surprised.' He studied her face for another moment, brow creasing. 'Can anything be so difficult to explain?'

The tremor that ran through her had nothing to do with being chilled. 'Yes, it's difficult. Sitting here like this isn't making things any easier either. Supposing somebody else took it into their heads to come down for a swim?'

He wasted no time in protesting the unlikelihood. Watching him stride across to secure both her robe and his own, Lynn could only admire his total lack of self-consciousness. Falling in love with him had been inevitable; hiding from it was no longer possible. The most she could hope for was to keep her secret, because he almost certainly didn't feel the same way about her.

'You're coming upstairs with me,' he stated unequivocally when they were both decently covered. 'You were right, we can't talk here.'

It wasn't what she had said but she let it pass. Hands nerveless, she bent down and scooped the two halves of her bikini from the side where he had tossed them, wringing them out before stuffing them into her pockets. She had no idea what the time was, but the night porter could quite well be on the desk when they went through. Last night or not, she wanted no stories of nude bathing parties flashed around the breakfast tables.

They made the lifts without seeing a soul. Lynn had the feeling that whoever was on duty was going to find himself in trouble come the morning for being absent from his post. The lift itself seemed to make an awful racket in the quietness of the night. She was relieved when it came to a halt and they could get out, although dreading the coming confrontation. Andreas was going to be satisfied with no less than the truth; what his reaction would be she hated to think.

A solitary lamp had been left burning in the suite's sitting room. Andreas led the way through to a plain white bathroom and selected a couple of towels from those folded over the rail, handing one of them to her. 'Dry your hair,' he said. 'It's dripping down your collar. Would you like a drink of anything?'

Lynn shook her head. Alcohol wasn't going to help. She rubbed her hair until the worst of the moisture was gone, knowing full well she was playing for time. He was standing at the balcony doors when she eventually went back through, the towel he had used slung over a nearby chair. He turned to look at her, eyes dropping for a brief moment to her bare thighs before coming back to her face in obvious resolution. This was one time when sex was not going to get in the way.

'Sit down,' he invited.

'I'd rather stand.' Lynn bit her lip, aware that the time was now yet still reluctant to take the step. The words came slowly. 'Does the name Caroline Brent mean anything to you?'

If there had been even the faintest doubt left in her mind, the sudden freezing of expression was all the confirmation needed. Heart heavy, she watched the adjustment taking place—the dawning of realisation.

'I should have known the resemblance was too marked to be accidental,' he said brusquely. 'Who are you?'

'Her sister. Brent is her married name.' She found it difficult to go on. 'You did know she was married?'

'Yes, I knew.'

'It made no difference?'

'It would have done if I'd known from the start. There are plenty of single, willing women around without running after other men's wives!' He studied her in silence for a moment, eyes cold. 'Was this planned between the two of you?'

'No,' she denied. 'Of course not!'

'You expect me to believe it was pure coincidence that you happened to choose the Amalia to spend your holiday?'

Lynn lifted her shoulders wryly. 'I found it difficult enough myself, but it's the truth. Caro only said you'd gone missing, not that you'd come back to Greece.'

'So she returned to England?'

'Not yet.' She watched him carefully. 'She's waiting for the divorce to come through.'

A muscle jerked at the corner of his mouth. 'You're saying I was the cause?'

'No one else. Reece wouldn't have her back.'

Dark eyes narrowed. 'I wasn't aware she'd left him.'

'Probably because you'd already left yourself before she could tell you.' Lynn made herself go on. 'Would you have brought her here with you if she'd caught you in time?'

The reply came short and sharp. 'No.'

She gazed at him, trying to see into his mind. 'Because you didn't love her?'

His jawline hardened again. 'We had some good times together without any ties on either side—or so I thought. When she told me she was married I just wanted out. The summons home came at the right moment.'

'For you perhaps but not for her.' Lynn scarcely knew whether to believe him or not. A man might conceivably deny ever having loved a woman who had hurt him badly enough. The intimation that her own physical resemblance to her sister had sparked off a form of retaliation could confirm that theory. 'You should have made things clearer for her if that was the case,' she added. 'It might have saved her marriage.'

'It might.' He was watching her with growing calculation. 'If you suspected who I was from the first, why didn't you bring it out into the open then?'

It was the question she had been dreading; the one to which she had no reasonable answer. She said lamely, 'I wasn't certain.'

'You mean you had some idea of making me pay for what I'd supposedly done to your sister?'

'Perhaps in the beginning,' she admitted with reluctance.

'How exactly?' His mouth was slanted. 'By making me want you then turning me down?'

'Something like that, I suppose.'

'It didn't work out so well, did it.' It was a statement not a question. 'I might even count it as a compliment of a kind.' He paused, regard rock hard. 'I take it you started feeling guilty for indulging last night, hence the sudden aversion. It didn't last too long.'

Her chin lifted. 'You didn't give me any option just

now. If I hadn't responded you were ready to force me.'

'That was an option.'

'Hardly a fair one.'

Broad shoulders moved in a shrug. 'I needed a vent.'

Lynn needed one, too, if not in quite the same way. She was no closer to knowing how he really felt about Caro. Telling him about saying her name in his sleep would serve no good purpose; he had already supplied his own explanation for her reaction. He was wrong, though. Guilt had not been the ruling emotion.

'I'd better be going,' she said numbly. 'We're leaving for the airport at ten.'

'I'm not stopping you.' There was no softening of attitude. 'There's little enough left of the night.'

She made a small gesture of appeal. 'We could at least part friends.'

'In civilised fashion?' He shook his head. 'I don't feel friendly towards you, Lynn.'

Which left nothing more to be said, she conceded.

She took the stairs down to her own floor. The sky was already beginning to shade grey when she finally slid into bed. Lying there, she tried to think positively about the immediate future. Perhaps she should consider asking for that transfer. Another whole summer negotiating London's traffic was a daunting thought. The five-day mini-tours should be interesting, if she could wangle it. American visitors seemed to prefer the chauffeured car to the coach. With every route tailored to meet individual needs, there would certainly be no lack of variety.

It was no use, she acknowledged in the end. Andreas wasn't going to be banished that easily. She allowed her mind to conjure up the rugged features, the hard masculinity of his body; to luxuriate for a moment or two in the memory of how it felt to be in his arms. If Caro had experienced this same aching need she could sympathise. Unrequited love was not to be recommended.

CHAPTER EIGHT

JUNE was a dry month with temperatures way above the seasonal average. The thunderstorms and resulting countrywide break in the weather during the first week in July helped top up the reservoirs but did little for tourism. Lynn was far from being the only one glad to see the sun out again. London in the rain was as depressing as any other city.

The application for transfer had not after all been submitted. Driving visitors around the capital and its environs was an all-seasons job, the other wasn't. There were worse ways of earning a living anyway, she told herself. Her earnings at the bank might have been higher but the interest had been at a very low percentage. At least in this job there was a regular change of both scene and faces.

Quite often now she was getting parties asking for her by name via recommendations from previous satisfied customers. It earned her both approval from the office and some substantial tips. The latter she banked against the proverbial rainy day. There was another winter to get through yet.

Life took on a certain new zest with the advent of a newcomer in the flat next door to hers. Daniel Peters was in his mid-twenties and a very junior accountant—though with excellent prospects, as he cheerfully assured her that very first night when he came round to borrow some coffee.

Good as he was with figures, his housekeeping left a lot to be desired. Inside a couple of weeks they were sharing an evening meal most nights. As Lynn drily declared after finding herself minus her salt shaker for the third time, it was easier to cook for two and split the cost than to keep a tally on his borrowings. There was nothing heavy about the relationship. They enjoyed each other's company but romance was strictly low key. Lynn drew no comparisons; there were none to draw. Daniel was as different from Andreas as chalk from cheese.

The one weekend she spent at home was not a success. Her parents were preoccupied with their elder daughter's marital problems. Caroline still hadn't said for sure what her plans for the future were, although she had intimated the likelihood of a visit to old haunts at some not too-distant date.

Lynn had already resolved not to mention her own meeting with Andreas if and when she saw her sister again because there was nothing to be gained by it. Memory had faded a little as the weeks passed. When she thought of him now it was with nostalgia but no particular pain. Her life was too full to allow time for regrets.

Summer came back halfway through July, bringing with it a whole new influx of eager-to-see-everything foreigners to the city. Lynn liked the full-day hires because they called for more variety—perhaps a morning shopping and the afternoon visiting places of interest. Her passengers usually came in pairs or family groups, but she occasionally drove the lone traveller, so it came as no especial surprise that Friday morning to be told she was to pick up a man at his hotel. It was the name that stopped her in her tracks.

A swift check of the work sheet confirmed the matter. There might be other A. Stephanos in London, but it was unlikely that this one would turn out to be a stranger. She had told him who she worked for. All he would have needed to do was look it up in the directory.

'Nothing wrong, is there?' asked the controller when she failed to move from the desk straight away. 'He asked for you by name.'

'Canadian accent?' she queried, just to be sure.

'That's right.' He was looking at her curiously. 'Thought it sounded odd considering the name. Know him, do you?'

'Someone I met in May.' Lynn hesitated, not at all certain of her exact emotions at this moment. 'I don't suppose there's any chance of doing a swap with one of the others?'

'All out, I'm afraid.' Bushy brows drew together. 'Something funny about him?'

'No, nothing like that.' She smiled and shrugged. 'It isn't important. I'd better be on my way. See you later, Joe.'

Her thoughts were going around in circles as she went down to the garage. Andreas had to be here in London for a purpose, but what? Why bother looking her up when they had parted on such inimical terms? She had thought herself over him, yet here she was now, heart thudding like a trip hammer at the very notion of seeing him again. She had to get a hold of herself before they did meet, that was for certain. He must never guess what she had gone through because of him those first days back.

The silver-blue fleet car was ready for her, freshly valeted and with a full tank. Lynn took a swift glance at her reflection in the driving mirror before setting off, adjusting the peaked cap to a jauntier angle. She still had a tan, though the sun-bleached streaks in her hair were fading. Her eyes were emerald bright with anticipation, bringing a wry smile to her lips. Damn Andreas for doing this when she had been getting on so well!

Traffic conditions held her up. By the time she

turned into Brook Street it was already approaching the half hour. He was standing talking with the commissionaire by the main doors of the hotel, shoulders broad beneath the casual suede jacket. Lynn brought the car to a halt at the kerbside and got out, meeting the dark eyes without a flicker.

'Sorry I'm late, sir,' she said formally for the other man's benefit. 'The traffic is heavy this morning.'

Andreas lifted an eyebrow but went along with the act. 'It isn't important.' He moved forward as he spoke, shaking his head as she made to open the rear door. 'I'll ride up front.'

Lynn saw him seated before going round to slide into the driving seat. She felt surprisingly cool and calm now the moment was here. He was just a man she had once known, that was all. Intimately, perhaps, but it was all in the past.

'Where first?' she asked.

'Anywhere you like,' he said. 'Out of the city for preference.'

'Windsor?' she suggested, and he nodded.

'As good a place as any.'

He was silent while she negotiated the turn out into the main stream, but she could feel him watching her. 'You drive well,' he commented after a few minutes. 'For a woman, that is.'

She gave him a swift glance, relaxing again when she saw the quirk at the corner of his lips. 'Women are the safest drivers according to the insurance companies, didn't you know that?'

'No,' he admitted. 'And in the majority of cases I wouldn't be prepared to take that statement at face value, either.' He was still looking at her, openly studying her profile. 'You seem different from the way I remember you,' he added on a curious note.

'I am different.' Lynn kept her own eyes on the

traffic ahead. 'It was another time, another place—as the saying goes. What brings you to England?'

'Business. I'm here to finalise the sale.'

'The whole group?'

'No, just the three I told you about. I decided to diversify my interests—as the saying goes.'

The irony got through but she refused to react. She said steadily, 'I hope your mother's well.'

'She's fine. She sends her regards.'

He was being polite, Lynn reckoned. Even if this meeting had been planned, he would hardly have bothered telling his mother. He was here on business. She was simply a passing whim. Keep telling herself that and she wasn't going to be disappointed.

Windsor was over-run. Andreas duly admired the castle's famous skyline but declined to take the tour. What he would really like to do, he said, was to find some good place where they could relax over a drink before lunch. If he was paying for her time, he added when she demurred, he was surely entitled to ask her to eat with him.

Lynn took him to an old coaching inn near Runnymede, leaving her cap in the car to accompany him through to the gardens at the rear, yet still feeling overdressed in her dark skirt and plain white blouse. Andreas had taken off his jacket, his open-necked shirt and pale beige slacks sitting easily on his muscular frame. Facing him across the wrought iron table as she sipped at the orange juice she had ordered, Lynn wondered at her ability to dissemble. No one watching them could possibly imagine the state of her mind at this moment.

'This is nice,' she said brightly. 'Quite unexpected, but . . . nice.'

'You just said that.' His tone was mild. 'Are we going to be reduced to making conversation for the sake of it? I booked this tour because I had to see you again and it seemed the easiest way. I'd suggest we start again from there.'

'Why?' she demanded. 'It's been almost two months, and we hardly parted on friendly terms.'

'I handled the situation badly,' he admitted. 'You gave me a shock and I reacted to it by instinct.'

Lynn gazed at him, conscious of her own warring instincts. She could read nothing from his expression, but then she never had been able to; not unless he had wished her to know what he was thinking at any given time. She didn't know what to say—what he wanted her to say. He was only here on a flying visit. What difference could it make now?

She put her thoughts into words not too well-chosen. 'If it's another brief encounter you had in mind you'll have to try elsewhere.'

'If that was all I had in mind I *would* try elsewhere.' He paused briefly. 'I don't have any urgent need to get back to Athens. We have time and to spare.'

He had said that once before, she reminded herself, and look where they had finished. Whatever his motives in looking her up, Caro was still right there between them.

'Your sister was in the past,' he said, accurately guessing her thoughts. 'Can't we leave her there?' One hand reached out to cover hers, the touch light but warm. There was no mockery in his eyes. 'I shouldn't have let you go, Lynn. Not the way I did. We shared something that was worth preserving.'

She made no attempt to remove the hand he was holding; that would have been too much of a giveaway. 'It was just a holiday romance that went wrong,' she stated flatly. 'Don't try to make out it was anything more.'

'I'm here now,' he pointed out. 'Doesn't that have

any bearing? I could just as easily have left things the way they were.'

'I wish you had.'

'You don't mean that. At least, I hope you don't.' The strong fingers were curled over her palm, his thumb softly stroking the back of her hand, turning her legs to jelly. 'I only came at all because of you.'

'The contracts . . .' she began, but he shook his head.

'It wasn't essential for me to appear in person. That was just an excuse.' His smile had a certain wryness. 'I've spent the last few weeks trying to forget you, only it didn't work out. Supposing we do as I suggested and start again from there.'

The arrival of the waiter with their two ploughman's platters forestalled any reply she might have made. Lynn slid her hand from beneath his and shook out the large paper napkin to spread across her lap. Only when the youth had moved on to serve another table did she say carefully, 'How did you and Caro meet?'

'In the bar of the hotel I was managing at the time. She asked me to light her cigarette.'

'She was there on her own?'

'Obviously. One of the reasons I went over. I thought . . .' he hesitated, glancing across at her, then decided to finish it. 'I suspected one of the porters was running a call-girl racket and I needed proof.'

Lynn was shocked. 'You actually thought she was a prostitute!'

'Some of them are very high class, and it wasn't the kind of bar women normally frequent on their own.' There was no apology in his voice. 'She said her date had let her down, so I asked her to have a drink with me. She began coming in regularly after that.'

'So you decided she was ripe for an affair.'

'The decision was mutual,' he said drily. 'She's several years older than you, isn't she?'

'Only three. She was married when she was my age.'
Lynn watched his eyes. 'The divorce came through
last week.'

'I'm supposed to feel guilty about that? If it hadn't
been me it would have been some other man. Women
like your sister crave change.'

'Except that you, she loved.'

His regard remained steady. 'She told you that?'

'Yes.'

'I thought she was still in Canada?'

'There are such things as letters. She wrote to me
after you vanished.'

'Pouring out her heart to little sister. Was that
usual?'

'No,' Lynn admitted. 'That's how I knew it had
gone deep with her.'

He shrugged. 'She must have loved her husband
once—unless she married him for other reasons. In
any case, it doesn't put any onus on me.' There was a
pause while he considered the untouched plate in front
of him, a frown creasing the space between his thick
brows. When he did look up again it was with a new
determination in the set of his jaw. 'I have to be
honest with you, Lynn. Learning she was married
didn't leave me entirely untouched. I felt I'd been
selected as a likely prospect. The first time I saw you
the resemblance got to me. Not just in looks, either.
You seemed to weighing me up. It took me some time
to realise you were nothing like your image. I should
have left you alone after that but I couldn't. I needed
to know you better.'

'You certainly achieved that.'

'No,' he denied, 'I didn't. Any more than you did
with me. Physical attraction kept getting in the way.
When you told me who you were it was like being
kicked in the teeth all over again.'

'*Philotimos*,' she murmured.

'To a great extent. It's inbred. It's taken me all these weeks to reach the conclusion that some things are more important than pride—for want of a better word.'

Lynn was silent for a moment or two, searching the hard-boned features opposite with mingled emotions. The word love hadn't been mentioned, yet that was what he appeared to be hinting at. No, she was wrong there, she thought with a sudden rush of insight. He was saying there could be more between them than simple lust, given the opportunity to develop. Real love came with knowledge of a person. In two weeks they had barely begun to plumb any depths. She had believed herself in love when they had parted but if there had been any depth to the emotion she wouldn't have got over it nearly as quickly.

'Say something,' Andreas urged, smiling a little at her intent expression. 'Anything will do.'

'Caro.' The name was dragged from her. 'She isn't going to go away.'

'But we can't let her get in the way, either. It was over before we met.'

'You think you could meet her again without feeling anything at all?'

'I wouldn't know that until we did meet,' he responded reasonably enough. 'There might be some initial awkwardness.'

It wasn't awkwardness she had been referring to, but there was no point in making an issue of it. The moment may never arise.

'You told me I'd changed when we first met,' she said, groping for some kind of assurance. 'Do you still think so now?'

'Not essentially. You've lost the insouciance. Perhaps it went with the cap.'

Her laugh came without forcing. 'I was trying to steer clear of any more entanglements.'

'There's been someone else since you came home?'

'No.' It was true so far as she assumed his meaning went. The gleam of his black hair in the sunlight made her fingers itch to touch, to feel the springing crispness beneath them. The effect he had on her was in no way dimished; she had simply been holding it in abeyance. If he was to be believed, he felt the same way. There was little reason to doubt his sincerity. He would hardly have gone to all this trouble unless he meant every word he had said. The question was, did she want to take him up on the offer?

'We've talked about it enough for now,' he stated, as if recognising the point her thoughts had reached. 'What time are you due back with the car?'

'We normally finish at five,' she said. 'Unless there's something special on.'

'And the weekends?'

'They're generally free, too. Most visitors seem to prefer weekdays for sightseeing.' She hesitated. 'I was planning on going home tomorrow. It's a month since I last went to see my parents.'

'Can it be postponed for a week?'

'I suppose so. They don't make any special preparation.'

'Then do it for me.' The smile that went with the request would have softened the hardest heart. 'Would you say there was any chance of getting the week off from work?'

'Not in a million. This is the busiest time of the year. Anyway, I've already taken all my holiday entitlement.'

'Just a thought. We'll have to make do with the evenings. At least we have two whole days coming up.' He took an experimental bite at a piece of Cheshire cheese, shaking his head. 'One taste I'll never acquire is for English cheeses. They're far too bland. You should import a few goats.'

'Try the Stilton,' she advised. 'It's good and ripe.' Her mood had lightened along with his. A week from now it might all be over again but at present that didn't matter. Just being together was enough to be going on with.

They drove out to Henley and spent a couple of hours on the river before returning to town. Lynn dropped Andreas off at his hotel and continued on to the depot, secure in the knowledge that she would be seeing him again in less than three hours. He would take a taxi to pick her up for dinner tonight, he had said, but tomorrow he would hire a car. She hadn't asked him what his plans were. Whatever he chose to do would suit her.

The same controller was still on duty. 'Everything go okay?' he asked as he took the sheets from her to check time and mileage. 'You seemed a bit worried this morning.'

'Everything's fine,' Lynn assured him. 'Absolutely fine!'

'Good.' He gave her a smile of paternal encouragement. 'He's a lucky man, whoever he is. Enjoy your weekend. Next week is booked solid.'

The tube was packed with people. By the time she finally arrived home it was almost half-past six. Her flat was little more, in actuality, than a glorified bedsitter, consisting of one largish room with bed-settee, plus a tiny kitchen reached through an archway, and an even tinier bathroom. The carpet of serviceable berber twist in mingled fawns had already been down, but Lynn had painted the walls herself in the palest apricot, and added curtains and cushion covers in varying shades of the same colours to create a scheme that was both cheering and reasonably practical. Her collection of framed miniatures and other bric-a-brac gleaned from happy hours spent around secondhand shops and market stalls brought character to the place.

She had hoped to catch Daniel before she started to get changed for the evening in order to tell him she was expecting someone round, but there was no answer to her knock. He could be working late, or have simply decided to stay on in town. Either way, it wasn't important.

Back in her room she took a shower, briefly regretting the lack of time in which to wash her hair, then put on a dress in a jade green, slub-textured polyster that looked like silk even if it didn't quite feel the same. By a quarter to eight she was ready and waiting, hair piled high, with casual tendrils escaping about her face and neck, nails freshly painted in dusky rose to match her lipstick.

The late sunlight made everything look better, she thought, viewing the street outside from the window. She had missed those soft, scented Greek evenings when the light was fading and the cicadas beginning to rouse from their afternoon stupor. Being on holiday in a place was different from living there, she knew, but it wouldn't be difficult to adapt. Home was where the heart was, and hers . . .

She pulled herself up at that point. Andreas had only just come back into her life. Any speculation about the future had to be premature. They might both of them find their feelings altered when it came down to it, although on this afternoon's showing the magnetism still existed. It remained to be seen what they made of this second chance.

He arrived a few minutes after eight. Lynn had seen the taxi from the window so there was time to give the room a final check before going to open the door. He was wearing a suit in a mid-grey lightweight cloth that subtly fined down his powerful physique. Sudden, unwonted shyness tied her tongue in knots.

'I let the taxi go,' he said. 'We can ring for another when we're ready to leave.' His glance encompassed the whole area without revealing a great deal, coming back to her as he added, 'The table is reserved for nine-thirty, but we can always change it if that's going to be too late for you. I forgot you weren't on holiday any longer.'

'I don't have to get up in the morning,' Lynn responded lightly, 'so it hardly matters. Sorry I can't offer you a drink—unless it's a glass of wine. I don't have any alcohol in.'

'I can wait.' He stood for a moment, eyes searching her face. Then he smiled slowly and held out a hand. 'Come here.'

Lynn went to him without hesitation, feeling the strangeness fade as she turned up her mouth to his kiss. The disciplined strength of his body was familiar. She leaned into it, drawing from him, gaining in confidence as she sensed his response. The run of his fingers down her spinal column made her shiver with remembered delight. She slid her hands under his jacket to trace the musculature beneath the smooth silk. They both had too many clothes on. She needed his warmth, his texture; the taste of him on her tongue.

'If we're going out,' he murmured, 'we'd perhaps better go now.'

What she might have answered to that was left open to doubt as something thudded against the outer door.

'It's me,' called a muffled voice. 'I've got my hands full!'

Meeting suddenly narrowed dark eyes, Lynn knew

her colour had risen. She made an apologetic little grimace. 'My next-door neighbour.'

'Then you'd better let him in,' he said, dropping his hands.

She moved to do so, summoning a smile as Daniel stepped into the room hugging a large and overflowing carrier bag at chest level, his briefcase dangling below.

'The darned handles went as I was coming up the stairs,' he gasped, heading for the nearest flat surface to dump his load with a sigh of relief. 'Thought I'd do my share for once and stock up for the week. Must have been mad to think I'd be the only one taking advantage of late-night opening!' He was turning as he spoke, the rueful grin fading as his eyes fell on the other man. 'Sorry. I didn't realise there was anyone else here.'

Lynn performed hasty introductions, finishing awkwardly, 'Andreas is taking me out to dinner. I thought you'd decided to stay in town.'

Daniel refrained from making the point that he never stayed in town Friday evenings; that for the past three at least they had eaten together then gone down to one of the local pubs for a drink and a chat. The two men made a contrast as they stood eyeing each other, both about the same height, but one as fair as the other was dark; finer boned throughout, Daniel was the first to break the small pause.

'I'll get out of your way then,' he said. 'We can sort this lot out tomorrow.'

'Give me your key and I'll open your door for you,' offered Lynn as he made to scoop up the carrier again. 'You won't be able to manage it.'

He took the key from his pocket and handed it over, glancing Andreas' way as he turned with the bag once more in his arms. 'Nice meeting you.'

Lynn preceded him along the corridor to the

adjoining door, fitting the key in the lock and stepping aside to hold the door ajar until he was through.

'Sorry about this,' she proffered uncomfortably, following him into the replica of her own kitchenette. 'He turned up out of the blue and I . . .'

'It's all right.' Daniel was taking things from the carrier as he spoke and putting them on the working surface. 'I don't have any claim on your time, Lynn. My fault for taking too much for granted.' His tone lightened. 'I'll have a meal down at the pub. Leave more stuff for next week.'

'I might be tied up most of it' she admitted. 'Andreas is staying.'

He glanced at her sharply. 'Here?'

'No, he's in a hotel.'

'You never mentioned him before.'

'We met when I was in Greece earlier this year. I didn't expect to see him again. It wasn't exactly . . .'

'Hey, you don't have to go into any detail.' The flippant note was back. 'We're just good friends, remember!'

It was what Lynn had thought herself until just now. Daniel's reaction was both discomfiting and disconcerting. She said lamely, 'See you later then.'

Andreas looked round from the window as she re-entered the room. Her heart sank at the expression on his face.

'You should have been honest with me,' he said. 'You told me there'd been no one else.'

'There hasn't,' she denied. 'Not in the sense you meant. Daniel is a neighbour and friend, that's all.'

'That wasn't the impression I got just now.'

'Then you were reading too much into too little. I sometimes cook for the two of us when we're both going to be in.'

Dark brows lifted. 'Sometimes?'

'All right then, most times. Daniel could burn water if left to it!'

'So you took pity on him.'

'Something like that, yes.' She switched suddenly from defence to attack, bristling with resentment at his tone. 'You can't just walk back into my life and expect to find me shunning all other company!'

'I didn't expect it,' he said. 'I'd simply have preferred prior warning.'

'Of what? There's nothing between us.'

He studied her for several seconds before stating flatly, 'If you believe that yourself, it isn't an opinion he shares. You must have given him some reason for feeling proprietorial about you.'

Lynn sighed, her flash of temper fading as swiftly as it had arisen. 'If I have it wasn't intended. We've only known each other a matter of a few weeks.'

His smile was faint. 'It took you a lot less than that to cement my interest.'

'That was different. I was trying.'

'Extremely.' There was another pause, then he inclined his head. 'Fifteen years can't alter basic nature. I'm pure possessive Greek when it comes to women. That's something you'd need to understand about me, Lynn.'

'I do,' she said softly, for the first time able to comprehend how he might have felt on discovering that her sister already had a husband. He wouldn't have had to be in love with her; the fact alone would have been enough. 'I really do.'

'Good.' He made a decisive movement towards the telephone table. 'I'll call that taxi.'

They spent the evening dining and dancing at the Latin Quarter. Watching the floor show, Lynn deliberated the question of what was to happen later, after they left this place. She was in no doubt about what she wanted; just being this close to Andreas again made her yearn for his lovemaking. What worried her most was where it was going to lead. He had followed her to London because, on his own admission, he had been unable to put her out of his mind, but that wasn't to say the feeling would develop into anything permanent. If the truth were known, she still wasn't sure she wanted it to. She had her own plans for the immediate future and they didn't include a serious relationship.

'You're looking pensive,' he observed quietly, startling her because she had thought his attention was concentrated on the showgirls on stage. 'Is something bothering you?'

Lynn shook her head, summoning a smile. 'I'm fine.'

Whether he believed her or not he let it go. She was probably worrying for nothing, anyway, she decided at length. Come the end of this week he had allocated he might very well conclude that they had too little in common to contemplate any further pursual. In the meantime, there was surely no harm in enjoying what they did have.

Dancing again after the show, she made no effort to conceal her ardour, melting into his arms during the slow numbers; feeling the pressure of his thighs against hers, the tensing of nerve and sinew as she breathed in his male scent. She knew every inch of this body of his, the way he knew hers; she remembered the way he looked, the play of muscle under his skin when he moved, the tapering breadth from shoulder to waist, the leanness of hip and tautness of thigh. Proud, even arrogant at times though he might be, he was a man any woman would be drawn to, both physically and emotionally.

'Are you ready to leave?' he asked softly, lips against her ear. 'It's almost one o'clock.'

'It's going to be nearer two before we get out to Clapham,' Lynn responded, suddenly at odds with herself again. 'You don't have to take me home. I'll be all right in a taxi.'

He drew back a little to look at her, brow tilted. 'Is that what you want?'

Her eyes were on his mouth, mind and senses battling. 'No,' she admitted.

'Then why make excuses? I thought we were past the need for pretence.'

She met his gaze, colour rising. 'You saw my flat. I don't have a separate bedroom. The sofa unfolds.'

'So?'

'So it's old and it creaks and it was never meant for two,' she got out, feeling gauche and embarrassed.

'And you have at least one neighbour you'd prefer not to disillusion any further.'

It would have been pointless to deny it. 'That comes into it, yes.' She tagged on swiftly, 'I never encouraged Daniel to think we . . .'

'You never let him kiss you?'

'Well, yes, but . . .'

'Then you encouraged him.' It was a statement of fact. 'I have a suite. Will you come back there?'

The rejection was instinctive, springing from some well of half-forgotten parental strictures. She bit it back, saying instead, 'You mean smuggle me in?'

His lips twitched. 'I hardly think that's going to be necessary.'

Lynn doubted it, too. It must be happening all the time. Providing there was no actual loss of revenue, hotel staff would turn a blind eye to unregistered guests—especially where it might prove advantageous on a personal level. Andreas was a generous tipper, she already knew.

None of which helped her decision.

'The question is,' he observed when she continued to hesitate, 'what you really want. I'm not pressuring you, Lynn. Making love to you tonight would be the icing on the cake, to capture a phrase, but it isn't the only reason I'm here.'

It was the tone of his voice as much as the words themselves that finally clinched the moment. She brought up a hand between them to lightly touch the firm lips. 'I want *you*,' she whispered.

At this hour of the morning it took them bare minutes to reach the hotel. Urged ahead through the revolving doors, Lynn knew a surge of relief on finding the lobby still fairly well populated. It was the first time in her life she had ever done anything like this, and she intended it to be the last. She wasn't cut out to be a woman-of-the-world.

They were on their own going up in the lift, but only when the outer door of the suite finally closed behind them did she really begin to feel safe from discovery. The sitting room was large and luxuriously furnished, the neutral colours of walls and fabrics an excellent background for rich dark wood. The two table lamps already switched on created intimate pools of light and shadow.

Warm breath stirred the tendrils of hair as Andreas put his lips to her nape. His hands were on her shoulders, fingers tenderly probing the sensitive nerves below her collar bone.

Desire rose in her, sharp and sweet, banishing any lost shred of reticence from her mind. It was she who turned towards him, lips blindly seeking; she who pressed her body close in urgent invitation. His jaw felt slightly rough, the way it had that other night, stimulating in its macho appeal. She rubbed her face along it pleasurably.

Andreas slid his arms out of his jacket sleeves in one

smooth movement, letting it fall to the floor at his back. Fingers not quite steady, Lynn rid him of his tie and unfastened the buttons of his shirt, laying tiny kisses across his bared chest. The long back zip of her dress opened on a whisper of sound. Easing the material over her shoulders and hips, he left the garment to drop free about her feet and brought his hands back up to circle her waist, kissing her temple, her cheekbone, her ear, his tongue an exquisite torment in its erotic exploration.

'I've missed you,' he murmured, holding her to him. 'Dear God, how I've missed you!'

Her, or someone like her? came the fleeting thought, pushed aside by the greater need as he lifted her in his arms.

The bedroom was illuminated by a single lamp. Lying on the bed where he laid her, Lynn watched his face as he unfastened each lacy suspender and drew off the gossamer fine stockings and then the belt itself, her whole body quivering when he dropped his head to gently kiss each inner thigh.

It took him bare moments to shed his own clothing, but it was too long. Tanned as she still was, his hands looked darker still against her skin, tracing the lines of her body with a touch that left fire in its wake, lingering to caress her breasts for a moment or two before sliding back down her flanks to span the soft warmth of her belly above the thin line of her briefs, the heat slowly penetrating, mingling with that already building inside her; making her tremble in anticipation of what was still to come.

Stretching both outer fingers, he hooked the elasticated band and slowly drew the garment down the length of her legs, following the same path with his lips while she writhed and moaned beneath him, finding every sensitive spot, every fluttering nerve;

undermining every last vestige of her control until she no longer had a mind or a will, just the single wanton urge. She spread her thighs to take him, her hips arching to counter the thrusting power in his loins; matching him stroke for stroke to a climax that left them both drained.

As before, he made no attempt to withdraw and move away, instead supporting the bulk of his weight on his arms as he brushed light kisses across her eyes and temples.

'No regrets?' he murmured. 'Not still wishing you'd gone straight home?'

Lynn laughed, her breath catching a little in her throat. 'Is that what I was doing?'

'Up to the moment when you turned to me out there, yes you were. I could feel the doubt in you.'

'But it didn't change your mind about bringing me back here with you, obviously.'

'No,' he agreed, 'it didn't. I was fairly sure I could make yours up for you once I got you here.'

'Only *fairly* sure?' she teased. 'That doesn't sound like the man I knew two months ago!'

He placed a final kiss at the corner of her mouth and rolled over on to his back, one hand resting lightly on her hipbone. 'The man you knew two months ago learned not to be too sure of anything any more. There's less chance of disappointment. And you didn't answer the question.'

'No regrets,' she said. 'How could I have? You make love superbly.'

'The performance is entirely dependent upon the instrument.' The tone was faintly ironic. 'With someone as responsive as you any man could be a virtuoso.'

'Except that I wouldn't necessarily respond to just any man.'

He shifted again, this time on to his side facing her, his hand moving up and across to fondle her breast. 'I hope not.'

He didn't speak again. A few minutes later his even breathing told Lynn he was asleep. She was almost there herself, mind drifting, body relaxed: satiated. Something depressing hovered on the fringe of her consciousness, but she let it stay there. Tomorrow would be soon enough to start sorting out her thoughts.

CHAPTER NINE

ANDREAS was still sound asleep when Lynn wakened at eight, his face buried in the pillow, an arm hanging over the side of the bed.

She got up as quietly as possible so as not to disturb him, gathering her scattered clothing together before moving across to the bathroom. Her dress was still on the floor in the sitting room. She would retrieve it after she had a shower. One good thing about man-made fabrics, they didn't crease like the real thing. She still had to get home.

The shower swept away any lingering cobwebs. Dried, she wrapped herself in another of the huge towels and went through to fetch her dress, picking up Andreas's jacket at the same time and folding it neatly over a chairback. It would need pressing before he wore it again, but that shouldn't present any difficulties. He was sure to have more than just the one suit with him anyway.

He was awake when she returned to the bedroom, a couple of pillows propping his shoulders.

'How long have you been up?' he asked.

'Not long.' She added, 'I switched on the coffee maker. It should be ready in a few minuites.'

'Which gives us time to say good morning,' he said, and held out a hand to her. 'Come on over here.'

Lynn went, sitting down on the edge of the bed to return his kiss. With his dark hair tousled and his jaw rough he could still set her pulses racing.

'You smell delicious,' he murmured, running the tips of his fingers along her bare shoulders. '*Je*

Reviens, isn't it?'

'Yes, it is.' She was surprised he should recognise it. 'I carry an atomiser in my purse. I'm afraid I had to borrow your toothbrush but I rinsed it out well.'

His lips twitched. 'I think we'll both survive. I'll take a shower and shave while you get dressed. I feel at a distinct disadvantage with stubble on my chin.'

Lynn rose again from the bed to allow him to throw back the covers, stomach muscles contracting as he stood up. Stubble or no stubble, she wished he would make love to her again. Both body and mind craved that particular delight.

She was dressed, and had the coffee ready by the time he came through to the sitting room. He was wearing a white towelling robe, his hair damp and curling, jaw clean-shaven.

'More convenient this way, I have to admit,' he observed, sitting down on a sofa with cup in hand. 'A woman carries most things she needs around with her.'

The voice of experience, she thought with a pang. There had been other women in his life apart from her sister. She wondered how Caro felt about him now—whether she still cared. More to the point, how did he really feel about her? Was she, Lynn, simply a substitute? Did he hope, through her, to meet up with Caro again? Only Andreas knew the answers to those questions, and she wasn't about to ask them. He was hardly likely to admit it even if it was the truth.

'So what would you like to do today?' he asked, breaking in on her thoughts. 'I have to arrange for a hire car, but that shouldn't take too long. We can have breakfast up here while we're waiting.'

Lynn shook her head. 'I'll need to go home and change my clothes first. It would be a better idea if I did that now, then you can pick me up later. I don't mind what we do. You choose.'

'If that's what you want.' He put the coffee cup down and got to his feet. 'I'll ask the desk to get you a taxi.'

'No, don't bother,' she said quickly. 'There's sure to be one available.' She drained her own cup and got up, picking up her handbag from the cushion at her side as she did so. 'It's going to be around lunchtime, I should think, before I see you.'

'We can make it lunchtime,' he agreed easily. 'We have the whole day. Say twelve-thirty.'

'Fine.' The constraint was ridiculous considering the way they had just spent the night, but knowing it didn't help. 'Twelve-thirty it is.'

Andreas smiled as she started towards the door, and moved to head her off. The kiss left her yearning for more but he didn't prolong the embrace.

Going down in the lift with several other people she felt certain they must guess what she had been up to, although there was nothing about her clothing that stated evening wear only. At least the lobby was busy enough to grant anonimity to any one person.

The doorman remembered her though. It was there in his eyes, in the knowing little smile when she asked him to call a taxi from the rank. Lynn told herself it wasn't important, and knew she lied. It was important to her. She tipped the man anyway, settling back thankfully into her seat as he closed the taxi door. Silly to be so concerned with what other people might think, perhaps, but it was impossible to alter one's basic nature overnight. She wouldn't be doing this again in a hurry, no matter what the incentive.

It was another lovely morning, and a busy one. The ride out to Clapham cost a small fortune in time spent idling through traffic jams as well as distance. Paying off the driver left her with barely five pounds in her purse to last out the weekend—unless she paid a visit to a cashpoint till. Not that she was going to need all that much, she reasoned. Andreas was hardly the kind of man with whom one suggested going dutch!

She was still smiling at the thought as she climbed the stairs to the first floor. Daniel's door was before her own. She had just passed it when it opened.

'I thought those were your footsteps,' he said. 'I've got someone waiting to see you.'

Lynn turned, meeting his eyes in some discomfiture. 'Who . . .' she began, then broke off abruptly as another figure appeared at his back.

'Hi!' greeted the newcomer. 'We were beginning to think you'd gone for good!'

Recovery was swift, on the surface, at any rate. 'You should have let me know you were coming,' she said with creditable steadiness. 'Is everything all right?'

'Couldn't be better.' Caroline smiled at the man beside her. 'Daniel here heard me hammering on your door and invited me in for coffee until you arrived. I came in on the early flight.'

'Thanks,' Lynn said awkwardly.

Daniel shrugged. 'No trouble. I'll get your cases, Caroline.'

'And there goes a disillusioned man,' murmured the latter as he vanished back into his room. 'Nice, too. I hope this other guy is worth it.'

'What makes you so sure I've been with a man?' Lynn demanded.

'Because he said you left with one last night and didn't come back. Just that, no details.' She sounded amused. 'You don't have to be defensive about it with me. You're a big girl now. Of course, the parents might not approve. But then they're not likely to find out. I certainly shan't be telling them.'

Daniel came back with the two suitcases, waiting until Lynn opened her door then hoisting them over the threshold. There was no censure that Lynn could detect in the glance he gave her in passing, more a kind of sad reproach. There was nothing she could say.

'It's a travesty to call these places flats,' Caroline remarked candidly the moment the door was closed. 'You don't even have a bedroom!'

'The rent's reasonable for London, and that's what counts more,' replied Lynn, determined not to let the criticism get to her. 'My salary doesn't stretch to anything bigger.' She made an effort to infuse welcome into her voice. 'We can cope for a night or two.'

'Oh, I shan't be staying. Not now. I may as well head straight for home and get it over. There's a train around one—or there used to be. I can be there by teatime.'

Lynn felt the tension in her diminish a little. She wasn't ready for any kind of confrontation. 'What are your plans?' she asked.

'I haven't any in particular.' Caroline sank to a seat in the one small armchair, grimacing at the protesting groan from the springs. 'Not that I intend spending too long in Richmond, either.'

'I'm surprised you're going back there at all—apart from a visit, that is.'

'I need a little time to get my act together. The settlement I got from Reece won't last for ever but the income will be useful.'

'He isn't paying you alimony?'

'Isn't that what I just said? Enforcing it would have been difficult from this side of the Atlantic, especially as I never took out Canadian citizenship. My lawyers advised me to go for the lump sum in cash.'

Lynn said softly, 'Could Reece afford it?'

'Oh, he had to sell the house and realise a few

investments, but he won't starve. He still has the business.'

'I was under the impression he was divorcing you. Didn't that make a difference?'

'He just wanted an excuse. I got my petition in first, citing his secretary. That little affair had been going on for months before I met Andreas, believe me.'

The use of the name brought tension back into the room, for Lynn at least. She viewed her sister with troubled mind. They shared the same hair, the same eye colour, the same basic bone structure, but not a great deal else. Caro had always been the one with all the confidence; the ability to turn any situation to her advantage. She could still do it, it seemed.

'I'm sorry,' she said lamely. 'I really thought you and Reece were made for each other.'

'So did I, initially. Only very few people live up to expectations.'

She had said it before she could stop herself. 'Apart from Andreas.'

'Even him. He let me down, didn't he?'

'Perhaps he couldn't take finding out you were already married.'

Caroline's brows drew together for a brief moment, then she smiled and shrugged. 'I certainly let it all out in that letter I wrote you! If I'd told him earlier we'd never have got off the ground floor. His kind need sole possession. Maybe it's a Greek trait. I wouldn't know.' She tagged on pointedly, 'I've time for a coffee before I go. Daniel hadn't got round to making it when we heard you coming up the stairs.'

'You hadn't been here very long then?' Lynn asked as she moved towards the kitchenette.

'No more than five or ten minutes. Just long enough to glean his feelings where you're concerned. He was worried about you.' She paused as if waiting for some response, coming to the archway when Lynn failed to make any. 'Is it serious?'

'I don't know yet.' Lynn finished spooning coffee into the percolator basket and put on the lid. 'It will take a few minutes,' she added unnecessarily, switching on at the point. 'Did you want anything to eat?'

'No thanks. I went over my calorie count for the morning on the plane at breakfast, such as it was.'

Lynn turned to glance at her sister, slim and shapely in the knitted cotton and silk mingle suit that must have cost a bomb. 'You don't need to diet.'

'I would if I didn't.' She was not to be distracted. 'Who is he, anyway?'

If ever there was a time for coming clean that time was now, but Lynn still fought it. 'I'd rather not talk about it,' she said. 'Not yet.'

Caroline eyed her for a moment before saying softly, 'Just tell me one thing, is he married?'

'No.' That much at least she could say with certainty. 'No, he isn't married.'

'Good. At least that's one problem you don't have to face. When will you be going home again?'

'Next weekend, hopefully.'

'So we'll have a chance for a heart to heart if you're feeling the need by then. I'm an expert on men, honey.'

Evidence belied that statement, Lynn reflected, turning back to take cups and saucers down from the cupboard. Experience didn't necessarily bring insight. She knew that herself, only too well.

Caroline left at noon. With her two suitcases gone from the middle of the floor, the flat seemed almost spacious. She was having the rest of her stuff sent direct, she had said. Even when they had both of them been living at home, her wardrobe had never been big enough to hold all her clothes, Lynn recalled. In many ways she hadn't altered at all.

With only a bare half hour before Andreas was due to arrive, she changed her dress for a white pleated skirt and tan blouse, knotting a Liberty print silk neckerchief at her throat. What she was going to say when she did see him she hadn't decided. Her mind felt as if it were going round in circles. Caro was free now, and available. Shouldn't she at least have given them both the chance to meet again? If he still carried any feeling for her sister it was surely better to know it than to live in doubt?

Except that doubt left hope alive, and that was something she needed. She might have persuaded herself that there were other things she wanted from life more than any one man, but it wasn't true. It hadn't been true from the moment she had met him again.

The knock on the door came earlier than anticipated. Going to open it, she found Daniel standing there with a cup in his hand and a sheepish expression on his face.

'I forgot to get sugar,' he said.

There had been a two-pound bag of the stuff on top of the carrier last night, but Lynn decided against mentioning it. 'I'll get you some,' she said, taking the cup from him.

He was still in the doorway when she returned. 'Going out again?' he asked.

'In a few minutes,' she acknowledged. She made a small weary gesture. 'Daniel . . .'

'I know what you're going to say, and you're right. I'm taking this far too personally.' He paused, smile rueful. 'The truth is, I didn't realise how much I'd come to take certain things for granted until last night when I walked in on the pair of you. Not your fault. I just wanted you to know that.'

'Thanks.' Lynn felt worse than ever. She wished he would go. Andreas would be here any moment.

'Anyway,' he said, 'you know where I am if and when.'

Meaning if and when she found herself in need of solace, she assumed as he moved away. But it would hardly be to Daniel she turned in that event. Not now. She was better going it alone.

Andreas topped the flight of stairs as the other door closed. He gave it a thoughtful glance in passing, but made no immediate comment.

'You should have an intercom system on that main door downstairs,' he said. 'Anyone could walk in.'

'The kind of system you're talking about costs a lot of money and would probably put the rents up,' she responded mildly. 'We all have our own key, but it's hardly practical to keep it locked during the day with visitors coming and going, so we just do it at night.'

'I suppose that's something.' He was looking at the two coffee cups she had forgotten to remove to the kitchen, brows drawing together. 'You were entertaining?'

'Just coffee.' Lynn gathered the offending items together. 'I'll rinse them for now and wash them properly later.'

He waited until she returned to the room before saying on a level note, 'You wouldn't lie to me, would you, Lynn?'

Only by omission, she thought in swift, silent guilt. To deny that Daniel had been inside the door this morning would only serve to invite speculation as to who had. 'I can't just turn him away,' she said. 'He's a friend.'

'And that means more to you than my feelings on the subject?'

'No.' She couldn't meet his eyes. 'But you won't always be here.'

'Neither will you, if I can help it.' He moved to her, turning her towards him so that she was forced to look at him. His expression was difficult to decipher. 'I meant to wait a few more days before we talked about it, but there's no time like the present. I think we should get married. And at the earliest opportunity.'

Coming without warning of any kind, the announcement left her speechless. For several moments she could only gaze at him, eyes wide and dark, a pulse throbbing at her temple.

'Why?' she got out at last. 'Because we're good together in bed?'

'That comes into it. It would have to.' His mouth curved. 'We share the same appetites.'

She shook her head, still unable to believe he was serious. 'It's only been twenty-four hours.'

'Not for me it hasn't. I already had it in mind when I left Athens.'

'You were that sure I'd jump at the chance?'

'No, I wasn't sure. As you said yourself, we didn't part on the best of terms.' He smoothed her cheek with the back of his hand. 'If you're going to say no, say it now. I hate suspense.'

Lynn steeled herself to resist the urge rising in her. 'There's one small matter you seem to have overlooked,' she said, trying to keep her voice steady. 'That's love.'

There was no reaction that she could see in his eyes. 'The kind you're talking about comes with time and compatibility. We have as much chance as any other couple of making it through the first twenty years. As to the other . . .'

He bent his head and found her mouth, making her tremble with swift flaring passion. Lynn melted against him, hands sliding up and over the broad shoulders, fingers creeping into his hair to hold him closer; feeling his hardness, his heat, his masculine strength. It could work, she thought blindly. It really could! How would she say no to this?

They made love right there on the floor, clothing scattered around them.

'You're beautiful,' Andreas stated softly afterwards when she lay with her fair hair spread across the carpet. 'Other men might want you but they're none of them going to have you. Not from this moment on.'

'I shan't want anyone else,' she denied. Her smile was slow, sensual in its recollection. 'I shan't need anyone else!'

'I'll make sure of it.' He kissed her lingeringly, then levered himself upright, holding out a hand. 'Come and take a shower with me.'

The bathroom seemed almost too tiny to hold the two of them together. Andreas turned on the shower over the bath and followed her in, drawing the curtain across to enclose them. Seizing the soap, he began to lather her body, starting at her throat and covering every inch of her, down over breast and hip and buttock while she stood there with half-closed eyes relishing the intimacy. When he had finished she did the same for him, fingers sliding over the strong clean lines, tracing each ridge of muscle, feeling the storm gathering again inside her.

The sensation when he drew her to him was exquisite, bodies smoothly sliding together, skin tingling as he turned up the flow to full force. There was nothing she wouldn't do for this man, she thought as the water gushed over them; no lengths to which she wouldn't go to make him happy. If Caro had meant anything to him in the past, it was her he wanted now.

They honeymooned in the Trossachs, staying a couple

of nights at one place then moving on to another with no definite plan in mind.

Lynn loved the wooded lochs and little pointed peaks, the long walks and lazy evenings. Even when rain blanketed out the scenery on two consecutive days, she was happy enough to stay indoors and make love through the dim afternoons, secure in their own little world.

It couldn't last, of course. She knew she was going to have to face things sometime. It had all been so rushed. Andreas had given her the one short week to pack up her old life in preparation for the new. He had not disputed her decision to keep the simple Register Office ceremony a purely private affair. She had even sensed a certain relief. Her letter home would have arrived the same day. A shock for all, but even more so for Caroline. Lynn could imagine what her sister's feelings must be. She planned to write again from Athens, this time to Caro separately. By the time they saw each other again the wounds might have healed.

Andreas had set no time limit on their wanderings. His announcement one morning that they should be thinking about getting back brought despondency in its wake.

'I'd like to spend longer this way, too,' he said, sensing her emotions. 'Unfortunately, I still have certain commitments.'

His mother being one of them, she thought, making an effort to shed any gloom.

'How do you think she'll have taken it?' she asked. 'Your mother, I mean. You did let her know?'

'I told her before I left. She'll be accustomed to the idea by now.' He smiled at her doubtful expression. 'She would rather I'd married a Greek girl if I had to marry at all, but she likes you well enough for an *Anghlos*. Anyway, I'm selfish enough to put my own interests first.'

She said softly, 'Even before mine?'

'They should be mutual.'

Which they were, she supposed, so far as her knowledge went. Sleeping with a man was not the 'open sesame' to his inner being. He had said it himself: it took years to know another person. With luck and effort combined they would have those years, though she found it difficult to look that far ahead. There were so many things they had never even discussed—such as children, for instance.

She had to smile at herself there. It was perhaps a bit premature to start thinking about starting a family on honeymoon.

'Where are we going to live?' she asked, pouring them both another cup of coffee from the pot left on the breakfast table.

'My apartment at the Hellas will be adequate till we find somewhere permanent,' he said. 'You'll enjoy Athens in the winter months.'

'You've given up the idea of buying a house on Poros?'

'Not necessarily. It will depend on future events.' He studied her for a moment, then came to some obvious decision. 'How long would it take you to pack? We could be in Glasgow in a couple of hours.'

There was no point in prolonging departure, Lynn had to agree. 'No time at all,' she said. 'Most of our things are still in the cases.'

He pushed his chair back from the table. 'I'll ring the airport.'

They were on their way in less than an hour, with seats booked on an afternoon flight. Lynn hadn't asked, but she assumed they would stay the night in London then travel on to Athens the following day, if they could get a flight. For the first time in almost three weeks she remembered her former plans for that return to Greece, never to come to fruition. She might not have got the job anyway, when it came down to it. There were others with the same ambitions. Her job now was to make this marriage work. Andreas might not love her in quite the same way she loved him, but there was enough there to give hope that he might one day.

The airport was crowded. Having turned in the hire car, they had forty minutes to wait for their flight to be called. Lynn went to buy a magazine, pausing on the way back to where she had left Andreas to check the departure board just in case there was any delay. She hadn't accompanied him to the desk so she didn't know the flight number, but so far as she could see, the next London flight wasn't for another two hours. Either Andreas had got it wrong, or the check-in desk had.

'I think you'd better check our tickets,' she said when she reached him. 'There's no London flight for ages yet.'

'We're not going to London,' he said. 'We're flying to Leeds, then driving to Richmond. There might not be another opportunity to introduce me to your family for some time.' He studied her quizzically, registering her frozen expression. 'You do want me to meet your family, don't you?'

'Of course.' She rallied with an effort. 'It's just that they won't be expecting us.'

'So go and ring them if you'd rather not surprise them. If they can't put us up we can always book into an hotel.' His own expression altered as she continued to stand there. 'You're not trying to tell me you didn't tell them about us yet? I thought you'd written a letter.'

'I did,' she admitted unhappily. 'That isn't the point.'

'Then what is? Do they have something against Greeks.'

'No, of course not. At least I don't think so.' Lynn lifted her shoulders, eyes flicking away from the all too perceptive gaze. 'I'd rather wait, that's all.'

'Look at me.' His tone was quiet but with an underlying firmness she couldn't ignore. 'Now, tell me the truth.'

The words came out thickly. 'Caro will be there.'

Momentarily his brows drew together. 'Since when?'

'Three weeks ago.'

'So why keep it a secret until now?'

She hesitated before answering. 'I thought it might make things awkward.'

'For me or for you?'

'For both of us.' Her gesture appealed for his understanding. 'She turned up without warning. I didn't know what to do for the best—how to explain things to her.'

He said slowly, 'You mean you saw her in London before we were married?'

'Only very briefly. She was waiting at the flat the morning I got back from your hotel. It was a complete surprise.'

'So you keep saying.' There was something in his eyes she couldn't fully define. 'You didn't trust me to leave her alone, is that it?'

Lynn bit her lip. 'I suppose you might say I couldn't take the competition,' she acknowledged, trying for a lighter note. 'After all, she knew you first.'

'You neither of you know me,' he clipped. 'You least of all!'

There was too much truth in that statement to try refuting it. She said numbly, 'Do you still intend going?'

His glance was aloof, flicking over her as if he had never seen her before. 'Why not? There's nothing like renewing old friendships!'

CHAPTER TEN

THEY landed in Leeds mid-afternoon, and set out immediately to complete the journey.

At Andreas' insistence, Lynn had telephoned her mother from Glasgow to prepare her for their arrival. The reproaches had been anticipated, but they had carried no particular reference to Caroline's feelings on the subject, from which she could only conclude that the latter had kept her own counsel. They were to stay at the house, of course, her mother had insisted. She would have supper ready for them when they got there.

Andreas had received the news without comment. He had spoken very little during the whole journey. Stealing a glance now at the impassive profile as he drove, Lynn wondered what he was thinking. Was he remembering the way things had been for him and Caro? Was he steeling himself to see her again? It wasn't going to be an easy meeting for any of them, and it was all her fault. She had been an idiot thinking she could get away with it. The reckoning had had to come sometime.

The house lay on the outskirts of the town. Mr and Mrs Renford were waiting for them in the hallway, having heard the car pull up. Andreas emerged from his abstraction to acknowledge introductions with an ease of manner Lynn only wished she could emulate. The best she could do was try to convey a mute apology.

'Where's Caro?' she asked, taking the bull by the horns.

It was her father who answered. 'She's in the living room pouring the drinks to toast the two of you with. I had sherry and spirits in but she thought it should be champagne for the occasion. She went out and bought a bottle herself.' He added chidingly, 'She was very hurt that you didn't mention your plans when she saw you in London.'

'Lynn didn't know then,' Andreas put in smoothly. 'I hadn't asked the question at the time.'

From his attitude, the older man found the whole matter beyond comprehension. Weddings were a family affair. His elder daughter's certainly had been. Lynn could imagine his thoughts. If that marriage hadn't worked what chance did this one stand? A few hours ago she had felt a fair degree of confidence. Now, she wasn't so sure.

They left the suitcases in the hall for the moment. Caroline was standing in front of the fireplace when they went through. She was wearing a black silk shirt with slim-fitting cream pants, her hair twisted into a deceptively casual knot on top of her head. There was just the faintest flicker in her eyes as she looked at Andreas.

'Welcome to the family,' she said.

Equally in control of his facial responses, he nodded back. 'Thanks.'

'The drinks are ready,' Caroline went on in the same light tones, indicating the tray on the coffee table. 'We should lose no time in toasting the newlyweds. Dad, it's up to you to make an appropriate speech.'

'Let's take it as said,' put in Lynn hastily as her father cleared his throat.

She forced herself to stand smilingly at Andreas' side while the toast was drunk, knowing the arm about her shoulders was there simply because it was expected of him. He had stepped so smoothly into the role Caro had handed him to play, but that wasn't to say he felt nothing. Her sister had never looked more poised, more attractive and, in Lynn's eyes at least, more desirable. She knew the old familiar sense of inadequacy; something she hadn't felt in almost three years. It had always been the same.

The feeling grew worse as the evening wore on. Mrs Renford served an excellent meal of tender lamb with all the trimmings, but Lynn could conjure little appetite. She refused the apple pie and cream which constituted dessert, settling for a coffee and a small brandy from her father's treasured stock.

Seated beside her on the chintzy sofa, Andreas seemed totally at ease, one leg hoisted comfortably across the other knee. Lynn had already said in her letter that he was involved in the hotel business. Her father was interested, plying his new son-in-law with questions. She got up after a while and went to stand at the window, looking out over the dale to the high fells and remembering the first time she had stepped out on to the balcony at the Amalia. It felt more like years than mere weeks away. She had been a different person then—a girl with her future all mapped out. She might have been better settling for that in the long run.

Caroline drifted over to where she stood, the gesture casual, as if seeking a quiet sisterly word.

'You knew who he was,' she stated without raising her voice above a murmur. 'That's why you wouldn't tell me his name that morning.'

'I guessed after a few days,' Lynn admitted. 'You never mentioned his last name but there were too many coincidences for it not to be the same man.'

'But that didn't stop you chasing after him.'

'I didn't chase after him.' Lynn was hard put to

keep her tone level. 'He came after me, all the way to England.'

'Was that before or after he knew about me—or didn't you bother telling him at all until you had him safely netted?'

'I told him the truth the last night I was in Greece. He still followed me.'

Caroline was silent for a moment or two, biting her lower lip. 'We look very similar,' she said at length. 'Have you thought about that?'

It had been there at the back of her mind since they met, Lynn could have told her, but she didn't because to say it was to confirm it. 'He knew you were divorced,' she said instead a little desperately. 'I . . .'

'But did he know I was back in England?' The other glanced sideways to assess reaction, her smile ironic. 'No, I guess not. You wouldn't have given him that much choice. I'm not blaming you. I'd probably have done the same myself. All's fair in love and war.'

It wasn't like that, Lynn wanted to say, only she couldn't because it had been exactly like that. Her throat felt constricted. Truth hurt—especially when it came to self-knowledge. She had been afraid to let him meet Caro again.

'What are you two whispering about?' asked Mrs Renford reprovingly. 'Lynn, why don't you take your things up to your room? You'll be staying a day or two, I hope?' The last to Andreas himself.

'Just the weekend,' he said. 'I have to be back in Athens by Tuesday.'

'Oh, well, you'll be able to come for longer next time, perhaps.'

'And you must come and see us once we settle where we're going to live,' he countered.

'That would be nice.' Her glance moved to her elder daughter as the latter moved away from the window.

'Isn't it an odd coincidence that you two should both have lived in the same city in Canada?'

'Isn't it?' agreed Caroline without inflection. 'We'll have to get together and exchange experiences, Andreas.'

He inclined his head in her direction. 'I look forward to it. Lynn, come and show me where to take the bags, will you?'

She led the way from the room and picked up her travel case, leaving the two suitcases for Andreas. The guest room was at the back of the house, across the landing from both her parents' and Caroline's rooms. Decorated in apple green and white, it was, like the rest of the house, in perfect order, the double duvet as smooth as virgin snow, pillows plumped to balloon-like snugness.

'The bathroom is next door,' she advised as he deposited his burden on the floor. 'You go on back down. I'll unpack what we're going to need for the weekend and leave the rest.'

He didn't move, standing there looking at her with an odd expression in his eyes. 'Have you always felt the same way about your sister?' he asked.

Lynn put her hand case down on the bed and opened it. 'Which way is that?'

'You know what I'm talking about. You resent her. It comes across from you in waves.'

Her shrug held a nonchalance she was far from feeling. 'If I'm that obvious, there isn't much use my denying it. Sibling jealousy isn't so rare an occurrence. According to what your mother told me, you weren't immune yourself.'

He ignored the latter comment. 'You're saying your parents treated the two of you differently?'

Lynn gave up the pretence of looking for something in the bag and sat down on the edge of the bed, meeting his gaze with wry acceptance. 'Not materially. I suppose it was mostly that Caro was always the clever one—the kind who never needed to try too hard to achieve anything. All through school I was expected to follow in her footsteps, only I couldn't. I was what they call a good average, not really shining at anything in particular. It was the same at home. Nothing I attempted was ever up to Caro's standard. The trouble was the harder I tried the less I succeeded. Eventually I simply gave up even attempting to compete.'

He said softly, 'Until you met me. You only became interested when you realised my connection with Caroline.'

'That isn't true!'

'Isn't it? You'd deny you spent the night with me on Poros purely to prove you were capable of matching up to her?'

'There was no more to it than that,' Lynn protested. 'I . . .'

'You weren't in love with me.' It was a statement not a question. 'Any more than you are now. I'm a means to an end.'

'That isn't true either.' She was doing her best to keep her tone level. 'If I'd wanted to flaunt you in Caro's face I'd have been the one to suggest coming here in the first place, wouldn't I?'

'Unless you couldn't bring yourself to do it in person. A letter from Athens would have been much easier, and just as effective.'

Anger washed through her suddenly, tensing her jaw. 'And your motives were always so pure, I suppose! From the first minute we met I reminded you of Caro, and what she'd done to your precious male pride. You didn't want me, you wanted revenge!'

He appeared unmoved by the accusation. 'So we were both deluding ourselves.'

The anger faded as swiftly as it had arisen. She said tonelessly, 'So what do we do now?'

'Exactly as we were going to do. On Monday we fly to Athens. My mother will be expecting us.'

'And then?'

He shrugged. 'We still have enough going for us to make a fresh start.'

'You mean in bed?'

His smile was sardonic. 'It's as good a place as any to cement a marriage. Do your unpacking. I'll go back downstairs and continue getting to know your family.'

Lynn sat for some time after he had gone, just staring at nothing. This should be one of the happiest times of her life, she thought ruefully. It had been up until today. Andreas was right in part: she had felt a certain triumph in achievement when he had asked her to marry him. But he was wrong when he said she didn't love him. The emotion was ripping her apart.

The two men had gone out to visit one of the local public houses when she went downstairs again.

'Dad thought Andreas might appreciate a comparison,' explained Caro blandly. 'You didn't want to go with them, did you?'

Lynn shook her head. 'No more than you would.' She glanced at her mother who was busy unravelling wool from an old sweater, added on a tentative note, 'Am I forgiven?'

'Of course, dear.' Mrs Renford didn't look up. 'It's not what we'd have chosen given the opportunity, but there you are. Greece isn't as far away as Canada. You'll be able to visit fairly regularly, I should think.'

'And you'll accept Andreas' invitation?'

'Well, we'll have to see about that. You know how your father is about travelling.'

'I'll come and visit you,' offered Caroline.

'Now that's a good idea,' approved her mother. 'You're used to flying. You'll have to arrange it, the two of you. Perhaps in a month or so when you're settled, Lynn.'

Two pairs of green eyes met across the room. Lynn's were the first to fall. 'Why not?' she said.

The men came back at eleven no worse for wear. By eleven-thirty, with both her parents well past their normal bedtime, Lynn felt bound to make the first move. With her mother's injunction to sleep in as long as they liked ringing in her ears, and Caro's ironic glance still warming her skin, she mounted the stairs ahead of Andreas.

'You take first turn in the bathroom,' she invited at the top. 'I'll wait.'

'We've shared up until now,' he reminded her on a dry note. 'There's no reason to stop.'

'Except that we happen to be in my parents' home, and they might not appreciate that kind of togetherness,' she returned steadily. 'They were never what you'd call "with it".'

'I never referred to anyone or anything in my life as "with it",' he said. 'But I take your point. All right, I'll go first.'

Lynn had already hung his silk robe on the hook at the back of the bathroom door. When he came into the bedroom some minutes later he was wearing it and carrying the rest of his clothes. Conscious of the fact that the other three were tactfully waiting downstairs for them to finish, she settled for a wash instead of her customary bath, cleaning her teeth and running a cursory brush over her hair.

'All clear,' she called down the stairs before going back to the bedroom.

Andreas was in bed, the duvet pushed back to waist level. She knew he was naked; he didn't possess a pair of pyjamas. It was the first time in more than a week that she had worn a nightdress herself.

'Take it off,' he enjoined as she let her cotton wrap fall from her shoulders. 'We're past that stage.'

'You might be,' Lynn returned tautly, 'but I'm not. I can't act as if nothing's altered between us.'

'I still want you. That hasn't altered.'

'More than you want Caro?' she flashed. 'After all, we're physically alike.'

'Yes, you are. I hadn't realised just how much until I saw you together.' He paused a moment, studying her with enigmatic expression. 'That must have made things even more difficult for you when you were younger.'

It wasn't sympathy exactly, but it was close enough to disarm her. 'It increased the expectations, if that's what you mean. Were you like Dion?'

'We shared the same colouring, little else.' His tone dismissed the subject. 'Come to bed. Talking isn't going to get us anywhere.'

Short of sitting up all night in the one straight-backed chair, there was no other place to go. Lynn switched off the bedside light before sliding under the duvet, lying on her back as far to her own side as she could get without actually falling out. She heard Andreas sigh, and felt the mattress give as he shifted his weight towards her.

'Keeping me at a distance doesn't solve anything either,' he said, his hand seeking her breast. 'We have to build on what we have together.'

Right or wrong, she knew herself incapable of rejecting the overture. Not with her body already responding. The problems dissolved as his lips found hers. They would be back but she couldn't think about that now. She didn't want to think about anything, just to feel.

She was alone when she awoke. For a brief moment she actually thought she was back in the *taverna* on Poros until the familiar room swam into focus.

The light coming in through the partially drawn curtains had that early morning pearliness associated with a fine day to come. Glancing at the bedside clock, she saw it was only just after five-thirty. The only place Andreas could have gone at this hour was the bathroom. No one else would be up yet.

There was no sound from the landing. After ten minutes she got up and went to the door. The bathroom door was open, which excluded that as a possibility. She could hear nothing from downstairs.

Heart jerking in sudden dread, she turned back into the room, letting out her pent breath on a long sigh of relief when she saw the suitcase still standing beside her own in the far corner.

A pair of slacks and a light sweater were the only things missing from the wardrobe, plus the shoes he had worn the day before. He might have taken himself for a walk, she reasoned. In Scotland they had walked every morning before breakfast, although never quite as early as this. Perhaps he had needed to be alone for a while. She could appreciate that feeling. Making love with Andreas was still the most tumultuous experience of her life but could it last like that? What would happen to the two of them if and when the passion began fading, with nothing else to hold them together? For one person to love wasn't enough. It had to be both.

He hadn't returned by the time she was dressed. Moving quietly so as not to disturb her parents who rose at seven, Lynn went downstairs and let herself out of the kitchen door. The sun was gentle as yet, its rays only just beginning to top the surrounding trees. The massed beds of her father's prize roses wafted a sweet and heavy scent.

There was a gate at the bottom of the garden leading out on to the narrow back lane. She couldn't be sure that was the way he would have gone, but it seemed logical to suppose he would have chosen it in preference to the road at the front. She followed the lane down to the end of the line of houses and crossed the stile into the neighbouring field, hesitating at the junction of two paths cutting at right angles to each other across the grass. To the left lay the town. She and Caro had used this short cut to school in the days before Caro had transferred to the seniors. Three years later, Lynn had made the same move, though hardly with the same results. Two 'O' levels to her sister's eight, and neither of them especially good grades at that. The job she had held down in Richmond for four years had given her no satisfaction, even if she had been lucky to get it. Leaving home had probaby been the best thing she had ever done.

She took the right-hand path in the end, looking up at the moorland lofting into the clear blue sky. He wouldn't have gone that far surely. The thicket of trees that lay between hid the lower reaches. If he had come this way at all he was probably in there, perhaps on the verge of turning for home. What she was going to say to him when she saw him she wasn't sure. She just needed to be with him.

It was another quarter of an hour before she finally acknowledged defeat and turned back herself. Wherever Andreas had gone, he almost certainly hadn't chosen the same path or she would have come across him by now. Suspicion crept into her mind despite all her efforts to stop it. Supposing he had gone to Caro's room? Supposing he had wanted to discover just which sister appealed to him the most? Caro might have turned him away, but again she might not. All's fair in love and war, she had said last night. Andreas had been hers first after all.

She found the whole household up and dressed and in the kitchen when she opened the door. They turned as one to look at her with varying expressions.

'Where on earth have you been?' asked her mother on a note of irritation. 'Really, Lynn, it's too bad of you to worry everyone this way!'

'I went for a walk.' Lynn looked from Andreas to her sister and back again, no wiser for the exercise. 'I thought that's what you'd done,' she added, trying not to sound accusing. 'You were missing when I woke up.'

'I was out front in the garden,' he said. 'I went back upstairs about a quarter after six to see if you were awake, and found you gone.'

'He was waiting here and wondering when I came down,' put in Caroline smoothly. 'Seems you must have just missed each other. I'll start breakfast. No bacon and eggs for you, Andreas?'

On the surface she simply appeared to be taking it for granted that he would naturally prefer Continental. Only Lynn knew better. She was underlining her knowledge of him; her prior claim to intimacy. They must have spent at least one whole night together at some point of their relationship. And this morning? That was still open to speculation. They might not have actually made love but Caro had received some kind of morale boost. It was there in her very manner.

The day went through its phases. At Caroline's suggestion, the three of them drove into Richmond for the afternoon. Andreas was intrigued by the ancient church with shops built into its walls, by the network of little cobbled alleys and streets so different from anything either Greece or Canada could offer.

'A lovely place to grow up in,' he commented, standing on a grassy bank within the castle walls looking down on the river. 'So much history.'

'Nothing like yours,' responded Caroline. 'Your civilisation was in its heyday when we were still painting ourselves with woad!'

'Which makes our progress remarkable considering,' said Lynn shortly. She caught Andreas's eye and looked away again, aware that he recognised her need to pull Caro down. There had been no call for the snappy rejoinder.

They were in the market place when the two of them went missing. Lynn had paused to look at an antiques' stall. When she looked round she could see no sign of them among the weekend crowds. She spent twenty minutes pushing her way through the throngs in the hope of finding them before acknowledging the futility. The only thing to do was go back to the car and hope they would have the same idea.

Apparently they had thought of it first. She could see the pair of them standing by the side of it talking as she turned the corner of the street. Quashing the instinctive urge to hide and watch them, she went to join them, summoning a smile as they looked up and saw her.

'A real squash back there, wasn't it?' she said brightly. 'Like looking for a needle in a haystack!'

'That's what we thought,' agreed Caroline. 'Only we were beginning to despair of ever seeing you again. We've been here a good ten minutes.'

'Ah, but you're brighter than I am.' Lynn opened the rear door, keeping the smile firmly on her face. 'I had the front seat coming, you have it going back. Share and share alike, isn't that what sisters do?'

Caroline shrugged good humouredly and got into the car. Andreas made no comment but the tension in his jaw was indicative. Already Lynn regretted the remark. She hadn't intended to make it; the words had formed themselves. She was turning into a jealous shrew, she thought miserably. If she wanted to drive Andreas back into Caro's arms there was no surer way.

It was another quiet evening. The five of them spent part of it playing scrabble, with Caroline taking the most points as usual. Unfair on Andreas, she declared after winning the third consecutive game. He should be given a consolation prize.

He had married the consolation prize, thought Lynn, watching his face as he made some appropriately light response to the offer. And he realised it. He and Caro were so much more attuned.

She was glad when her father suggested another visit to the pub for the last half hour, simply because it got Andreas out of the house for a spell. She decided to wash her hair while he was gone. So far he hadn't said exactly when they were leaving, but she hoped it would be Sunday rather than Monday. Two more days of this would be more than she could stand. Away from Caro they might have a chance.

Fifteen minutes later, after towel-drying her hair, she sat down at the dressing-table to comb it through. In this light, and damp, it looked darker than normal. Perhaps she should try a colour rinse, she reflected. Anything to lessen the resemblance.

As if in direct response to the thought, the door behind her opened and her sister came into the room.

'This is likely to be the only opportunity we're going to get for a private talk,' declared the latter, sitting down on the bed edge. 'And don't switch that thing on or I'll pull the plug!'

Lynn laid the hand drier down again, meeting the other green eyes through the mirror. 'I thought we'd said it all last night.'

'What was said last night was said in the heat of the moment. You'd given us little enough warning you were coming.'

'It wasn't my idea,' Lynn admitted. 'Andreas made the decision.'

'Even after you told him I was going to be here?'

'I'd say that gave him even more reason to come.' She forced herself to carry on. 'He only wanted me because I look like you.'

'That's ridiculous!'

'Is it?' Lynn twisted on the stool to look directly at her sister. 'You suggested it yourself last night.'

'And I already told you to forget last night.'

'And today?'

'What about today?'

'He was with you this morning, wasn't he? Then there was this afternoon when you both went missing.'

Caroline sighed suddenly. 'You're becoming paranoid. He was in the kitchen this morning, just the way I said, and you were the one who went missing this afternoon. All right, so I slept with your husband before you did. Hard cheese! If you felt so strongly about it you should have given him the push as soon as you guessed who he was.'

'I tried,' Lynn acknowledged. 'It wasn't that easy.'

'So how do you think I feel? Right out of the blue comes this letter to say you're married to the man I knew in Canada—the man I told you about in the first place. I'm supposed to believe you didn't purposely set out to nail him—which I find very hard, I can tell you.'

The pause stretched between them. Lynn was the first to break it, voice rueful. 'There's probably a lot of truth in it—or was. All our lives I've envied you because everything seemed to come so easy to you.'

'All I had that you didn't was ambition. You've developed some since. Leaving Richmond was the first step.'

Lynn shook her head. 'It wasn't just that.'

'Oh, you were a defeatist at heart, I'll grant you that. I had to leave the country before you'd stir yourself to start trying.' She added hardily, 'You still are defeatist. You want it all handed to you on a platter. I fell and fell hard for Andreas, I don't mind admitting it. I was devastated when he walked out on me. I'm not going to pretend he doesn't do anything to me even now, but I'm not fool enough to think I could win him back. You're what he wants.'

'He told you that?'

'Not in so many words. He didn't need to. He married you, didn't he? He never suggested marriage to me even when he thought I was a free agent.'

Lynn said softly, 'How long did you know him altogether? It was already over when you wrote to me.'

'A couple of months. Does it matter?'

'I don't suppose it makes a lot of difference, no. I just wanted to know.'

'Just something else to haunt yourself with? For the record, I only saw him a couple of times a week. It was all I could manage without making Reece suspicious.' Her laugh had an edge. 'Don't know why I bothered really. We were washed up before ever I met Andreas. I was supposed to be meeting another man that night, only he didn't turn up. Andreas could recognise availability when he saw it. Believe me, on his side there was little more to it.'

'You believed there was at the time. You must have done to tell Reece you were leaving him.'

'I was deluding myself. I can appreciate it now if I couldn't then.' Caroline paused, studying her with growing exasperation. 'For heaven's sake, what does it take? The man loves you.'

It would take his actual use of the word, Lynn acknowledged numbly, and she was unlikely to hear it. Which left her with the one alternative. Accept the situation and make the best of it. Not all marriages were made in heaven.

'It will be all right,' she said. 'Providing you stay away. I know that sounds hard and nasty, and I don't want to hurt you, Caro, but I can't alter my nature to order.'

'Don't worry, I understand.' The smile was comforting. 'As a matter of fact, I'm not sure I could take seeing the two of you settled in your own home—perhaps raising a family. Remind me too much of what I might have had with Reece if we'd both tried a little harder. We've never been all that close as sisters go. It isn't going to be too much of a hardship not to see each other outside of the odd blue moon.'

Lynn's answering smile was shaky. 'Right now I feel closer to you than I've ever felt.'

'That's the way the cookie crumbles.' Caroline stood up as a door banged below. 'They're back, and you still have to dry your hair. I'll go make us all some coffee—or would you rather have tea?'

'Coffee will be fine, thanks. Andreas . . .' Lynn broke off with a wry little gesture. 'I don't need to tell you his preferences. You knew them before I did. And no, I'm not being snide. Just stating a fact. The sooner I learn to look at things realistically the better. See you in a few minutes.'

Alone again, she switched on the drier and began to play it over the long fair strands. She felt far from happy but there was a certain lessening of tension in the knowledge that Caro would not be making that threatened visit. Perhaps one day she might acquire the confidence to invite her—if she wanted to come. For the present it was enough to know they weren't enemies.

They left on the Monday morning to fly down to

London. There was time for lunch before taking the seats already booked on the afternoon flight to Athens.

They would be at the Hellas before dark, Andreas observed when they were in the air again, adding that he was looking forward to a leisurely dinner in their own apartment.

'What about your mother?' asked Lynn. 'Shouldn't we call in on her first?'

'Tomorrow,' he said, from which she gathered that he had had enough of family commitments for the moment. She couldn't blame him for that. The weekend must have been a strain for him, too.

Yesterday hadn't been so bad though. Even her mother had been moved to remark how much better she and Caro were getting along now they were adults. 'Caroline was the scholar,' she had overheard her telling Andreas, 'but Lynn was prettier. She came second in the Miss Pears contest when she was three. Everyone made so much of her. I'm afraid it made Caroline very jealous.'

It just went to show, Lynn reflected now, how different individual impressions could be. There was always the chance that she might have misread Andreas's motives. Slanting a glance at him as he listened with closed eyes to the classical tape on channel 8, she wondered how long it would be before the two of them could exchange thoughts freely. Somebody had to set the ball rolling; perhaps it should be her. Only not just yet. Give it a little time. That was one thing they hopefully weren't going to be short of.

The sun was almost touching the horizon when they landed. Despite the late hour, the August heat was oppressive. They took a taxi to the Hellas on Venizelos Avenue, an imposing pile of classical architecture Lynn had hitherto seen only from the outside.

The place boasted a nightclub along with its two restaurants. It also had a swimming pool, and beautiful gardens. Judging by the number of people in the lobby, they were doing good business, Lynn thought as she crossed to the lifts at Andreas' side. She could see heads bobbing as word went round the duty staff that the owner was in the hotel. Living here was going to feel strange. She hoped they would soon find a house.

Situated on the uppermost floor, the suite provided superb views out over the city from both sitting room and bedroom windows. As at the Amalia, there was a balcony, far enough above the still thronged streets to isolate it from traffic fumes. Floodlights outlined the Acropolis against a midnight blue sky where stars were just beginning to twinkle.

'A shower first, then we'll order dinner,' said Andreas as she came back into the spacious room. He finished thumbing through the pile of mail left on a side table, glancing across at her with a faint smile. 'How does it feel to be here as a resident instead of a tourist?'

'Unreal,' she admitted. 'It's going to take some getting used to. I hardly know Athens.'

'It won't take long. Tomorrow, after I keep my appointment, we'll go to lunch at Floca's and I'll introduce you to some people.'

I don't need anyone else, she wanted to say, only you. But the words stuck in her throat. 'That will be nice,' she managed lamely.'

'Yes, well, I'll go and take that shower.'

This was ridiculous, she thought as he disappeared into the bathroom. She was acting like a virgin bride on the first night of her honeymoon! That man in there was her husband and she loved him. If she found it difficult to tell him in so many words she could surely show him how she felt. Waiting would achieve nothing.

It took her bare moments to shed her clothing. She left it in a heap on the bedroom floor and followed him. The water was still running, the outline of his powerful physique visible through the opaque glass of the cabinet. He turned when she opened the door, water streaming over his shoulders and chest and clinging in droplets to the thick black curls.

'Is there room for another?' she asked.

He made no verbal answer, simply reached out and took her hand and drew her in to him. There was hunger in his lips, in his hands, in the surge of his body against her. Lynn held nothing back, moaning her need of him. The past didn't matter. It was just the two of them now.

The cabinet was too confining. Leaving the water still gushing from the showerhead, he seized several of the thick Turkish towels and threw them down on the bathroom floor, pressing her down beneath him. Wetness beaded her skin, glistening in the light until he licked each droplet away. When he took her it was as if her whole life had been geared towards this moment—this sense of total oneness.

'I've been a fool,' Lynn confessed some time later when they were dormant again. 'I almost let jealousy rob me of the most important thing in my life.' Her voice was soft, a little shaky with emotion. 'I can even feel grateful to Caro because if it hadn't been for her I might never have got to know you at all.'

The dark eyes were luminous, his hands tender. 'Yes, you would,' he said, 'You'd have liked me better, too.'

'Quicker, perhaps.'

'All right, quicker.' He kissed the end of her nose, then pushed himself upright, drawing her with him.

'Come on through to the bedroom. We'll be more comfortable.'

Lynn had noticed no discomfort but she went without demur. Andreas didn't bother drawing back the covers, lying down on top of the bed with her in his arms.

'I want to hold you for a little while,' he murmured. 'We can eat later.'

Lynn couldn't have cared less about eating at all. It was enough to be here like this. She tried not to let certain mental images form in her mind, but didn't quite succeed. She could be grateful to Caro, yes, but that still didn't stop her from feeling second best. There was only one thing that could, and he still hadn't actually said the words.

When he did speak it was almost reminiscently, as if he had been lying there going over the past weeks. 'There have been times,' he said, 'when I despaired of ever feeling this way about any woman. There's so much written and said about love, but there's nothing to touch the reality of it. I was wrong about those twenty years. It took me less than a week. Nothing could keep me from you in the end.'

Lynn said softly, 'You really never loved Caro?'

He looked deep into her eyes, his own dark but no longer impenetrable. 'It never occurred to me to even consider the possibility. I didn't like being drawn into that situation. It angered me enough to make me want to hit out at any green-eyed blonde who happened to cross my path. You gave the distinct impression you were considering my possiblities that first time I laid eyes on you.'

She smiled a little. 'I probably was, though not with any intention of doing anything about it. You don't still believe I followed you that night, do you?'

'No. Although it took me a while to convince myself

I'd made a mistake about you. I didn't trust my own senses.'

Lynn laughed, putting up a hand to touch his lips. 'You almost overwhelmed mine. I was disgusted with myself for actually being attracted to a man who could do what you did!'

'I've done worse to you since,' he pointed out with a glint. 'I haven't heard any complaints yet.'

'You're not likely to either.' Her breath caught in her throat as she looked at the strong, familiar features. 'Oh, God,' she said thickly, 'I do love you!'

Something seemed to give in him, as if some deep down tension had suddenly been relieved. The kiss was almost fierce. 'I thought you'd never get round to saying it,' he breathed unsteadily.

'But you must have known how I felt. I've made it so obvious.'

'You've made nothing obvious. I could rouse you, sure, but that's all I could be sure of. Why else do you think I was so cut up when I found out about Caroline coming home? Even more so when I realised how you really felt about her. I thought you'd said yes to me just to prove something to yourself.'

'And there I was thinking I was so transparent.' Her voice shook. 'You've probably no idea how absolutely and deliriously happy I am right this minute.'

He smiled then, bending his head once more to find her mouth. 'I think I may have,' he murmured against her lips. 'I think I just may have!'

SAY IT WITH ROMANCE

ROMANCE